Sheila Kitzinger was born and brought up in Somerset. After obtaining her L.G.S.M. for teaching drama and voice production, she studied social anthropology at Ruskin and St. Hugh's College, Oxford, and did research and teaching at the University of Edinburgh. Her B.Litt thesis was on race relations in Britain. From 1971–73 she held the Joost de Blank Award and did research on the problems facing West Indian mothers in Britain.

She has been preparing women for childbirth and developing her own Psychosexual Method since 1958, has lectured widely in North and South America, Scandinavia, South Africa, Australia and Western Europe, and has studied methods of childbirth education and styles of childbirth in cultures as different as those of the West Indies, East Germany and the Zulu tribe of South Africa. She teaches expectant parents for the National Childbirth Trust and is on its Panel of Advisers. She is also a member of the Board of Consultants of the International Childbirth Education Association. She is a member of the Royal Society of Medicine (Open Section).

Her other books include: *The Experience of Childbirth*; *Education and Counselling for Childbirth*; *Women as Mothers*; *The Place of Birth*; *The Good Birth Guide*; *Birth at Home* and *The Experience of Breastfeeding*. She has also made a set of cassette tapes *Journey Through Birth* (Julian Aston Productions) for couples wanting to practise together for childbirth, obtainable through the National Childbirth Trust.

Note to the reader:
He, she or it? With five daughters I spontaneously think of a baby as 'she', but decided to call the baby 'he' or 'it' simply to distinguish the child from the mother.

I should like to take this opportunity of thanking all the women, and their partners, who have sent in such vivid accounts of their experiences in labour; and the hundreds of other couples I have taught who also have helped me to learn a little more each time.

My thanks also go to my daughters, Celia, Tess, Nell, Polly and Jenny, who did the washing up and made their own beds (sometimes), when I was shut in my study.

S.K.

GIVING BIRTH

To Uwe

Giving Birth

Emotions in Childbirth

SHEILA KITZINGER

SPHERE BOOKS LIMITED
30/32 Gray's Inn Road, London, WC1X 8JL

First published in Great Britain in 1971 by Victor Gollancz Ltd
© Sheila Kitzinger, 1971, 1979
First Sphere Books edition 1973
This revised and expanded edition published in 1979

TRADE
MARK

Set in Intertype Times

Printed in Great Britain by
Hazell Watson & Viney Ltd,
Aylesbury, Bucks

THE FIRST PREGNANCY

You have become an earth thing with this growing.
You have become a rooted plant
coming to rest at last,
a stem staked under pressure
with the pyramid of years of wandering inverted
bearing on you where you meet the rock.
Sea-weeds live thus
free swimming in the first stage of their life-span;
atoms of hunger drifting in a sea unbordered as the
        universe,
and many believe they live then as they never will.
Many imagine that the ache of metamorphosis
as cruel as birth-pains,
that the forcing out of roots,
and the melting down into the surface
are but acts of pain unalloyed by the pulse of joy.
Many,
the rootless as myself
regard this binding to the rock as a god's own torture
stretching to fill the years with agony.
    Yet who can conceive the longing of the plankton
screwed in the stresses of the tide
and blindly wandering?
Never in all its years to see a landmark
like a refugee in a land erased by wartime,
never a star to find its way by
more than the faithless green sparks of the phosphorescence;
only the waiting in the anguish of the mission,
never to be fulfilled until it touches earth.
And when it is bound

clench-fisted in its root net,
then only then can it begin to live.
  What do we know but that Prometheus was bound
not by the vengeful god-head, but the thing itself;
planted, not chained into the rock by the creative act.

1970   Nick Messenger

CONTENTS

PART 1

CHAPTER ONE

BIRTH AS EXPERIENCE

The urgent questions that women ask about childbirth mostly stem from one basic one: *'What is it really like?'* – 'What do contractions feel like?' 'How shall I know when labour has started?' 'How much will it hurt?' 'How long does the first stage last?' 'When shall I go to the hospital or call the midwife?' and so on. Since labours vary so much, it is difficult to answer any of these queries with accuracy but if vague generalisations are proffered instead women feel, quite rightly, that the answers are irrelevant and evasive. That is why this book focuses on the rich variety of human experience in childbirth. What some women enjoy, others dislike. Sensations which bring pleasure to some are frightening or distressing for others. The unfolding pattern of childbirth can vary widely too, so that for some women labour is all over and the baby delivered inside a space of a few hours, while others labour right through the day and night and are still not fully dilated.

Women talk to each other, of course, sometimes describing with apparent relish each ache and pain and flaunting each obstetric difficulty as if it were a rosette, the prize of having suffered in labour, to be exhibited proudly in front of others who have not yet been put on trial. It often seems to me that pregnant women attract horror stories of this kind because they grow up almost totally ignorant of the subjective experience of birth, however much they may have studied the anatomy of the rabbit and diagrams of the female reproductive organs, and are so clearly longing to learn more and to have the mysteries of birth unveiled. It is as if we provide in Western culture a kind of initiation into adult womanhood during pregnancy by warning girls of possible

3

dangers and suffering to come, rather as initiation rites in tribal society involve the use of terrifying masks and ordeals to mark the threshold of adult status.

Doctors and midwives are rightly critical of 'old wives' tales' and urge their patients not to listen to them. I have even heard a doctor advise patients not to talk to other women at all about childbirth. I believe that this is entirely wrong. Women need to share their experiences and have support from others who are facing the same challenges. Yet many expectant mothers and new mothers are socially isolated. They have friends and work colleagues who have not yet started their families and who tend to be interested in very different things; if a woman goes on working till the seventh month she may find that she faces childbirth in three months' time knowing very little and with no one to talk to about it.

Yet it is not only what women tell each other. Everything that happens in the antenatal clinic and the whole atmosphere of health care during pregnancy in many hospitals produce their own potent rituals by stressing the dangers of childbirth. Sometimes the expectant mother is even warned that childbirth 'is only normal in retrospect'. Even the antenatal class may in some ways reinforce this awareness of danger if it does not provide sufficient opportunity for free discussion and for hearing from other women at first hand about what labour feels like.

Obstetrics have changed dramatically over the last twenty years. New machines and technical procedures detect any deviations from normality, and what is normal is a statistical curve, the partogram, to which labour is expected to conform. Although a margin is allowed on either side of the curve, the actual size of this margin is decided by the obstetrician, so that some allow only two hours' variation in the speed of dilatation of the cervix on either side of the curve whereas others allow four. The important thing to remember, however, is that there is a norm to which the labouring woman is expected to conform. The clinical experience of midwives about the very wide variety of childbirth and the labouring woman's own feelings are now considered unimportant compared with the record of the partogram. A good servant has become a bad master and an undoubtedly useful tool has come to dominate childbirth.

Birth is treated as if it were a pathological event rather than a normal life process and this has an effect on all those working professionally with childbearing women as well as on the women themselves. By concentrating almost exclusively in the training of obstetricians and midwives on the diagnosis and treatment of disease and malfunction and on intervention, our society has succeeded in producing professionals many of whom have never seen a natural birth and who know nothing of the skills of supporting the normal physiological process. It is important for those working in maternity care to understand labour also as women experience it and this is much more subtle than just saying 'It's painful' or 'It's painless'. So I hope that medical students and pupil midwives will feel that there is something in this book for them too. Account after account tells of the things that helped women in labour and of what they found important at the time and reveals their hopes and fears so vividly that they convey with more directness than any textbook a great deal about the psychology of childbirth.

It is important that neither the father nor the mother approaches this book as if it could show them how one 'ought' to have a baby.

Here are first-hand accounts of women's experiences during the exciting journey of discovery which is labour, a journey which is unique for each person venturing on it. In these accounts I have tried to select reports which do not necessarily tell of easy labours, but which reflect the personalities of the writers: some 'feet on the ground' – practical, unemotional and matter-of-fact; others passionate, totally involved and caught up in a drama of Wagnerian magnitude.

I believe that this is one of the important things about preparation for childbirth – that it should not simply superimpose a series of techniques, conditioned responses to stimuli, on the labouring woman, but that it can be a truly creative act, in which she spontaneously expresses herself and the sort of person she is.

Education for birth consists not, as some would have it, of 'conditioning', but aims at giving a woman the means by which she can express her own personality creatively in childbirth.

There is no such thing as a 'text-book labour'. Each one is different, and brings its own problems, challenges, satisfaction and joy – in much the same way that a marriage itself, which may be superficially like any other marriage, is a unique relationship between two unique people. Education for childbirth and parenthood involves not only exercises and explanations, intellectual information and physical training, but – ideally – an emotional awakening which brings with it increased self-realisation and deeper understanding of a whole network of human relationships extending from the marriage and the family into the surrounding society.

Nor is it my intention to suggest that it is only births for which the mother has had previous antenatal instruction that can be happy. By chance or temperament, or because they are physically healthy, a great many women have fairly quick, efficient and non-traumatic labours.

But prepared childbirth is something else again. It may be 'natural' or 'unnatural', depending on whether extra obstetric help is needed, can be long or short, difficult or easy. Sometimes a forceps delivery or a vacuum extraction will be necessary – sometimes a Caesarean section. The point is that either way the woman in labour is co-operating with her own body and with her obstetric attendants to give birth to a live, healthy child, and she can do this better because she is acting with understanding, fearlessness and control.

This book is written not only for expectant mothers, but for men too. Having a baby is a joint enterprise, and there are a good many things about his pregnant wife that a man can never begin to understand if he does not take time to think about what her pregnancy and the coming baby mean to her, and some of the inner experiences through which she may be passing, as well as the events of labour, and what she can learn to do to be 'in tune' with her body during the processes of dilatation and expulsion.

Expectant fathers also want to learn how they can help in labour. They can get some of the more obvious things in antenatal classes – rub her back, tell her she is doing well, place a sponge soaked in ice water at her lips – but there are a great many other things that couples have discovered by chance were right for them at the time which are described in these pages. So this book is for men who want to be well-prepared too. It is important for the man to be flexible and sensitive to what the woman wants, and yet strong, so that when she enters the stress period of the late first stage she can rely on firm guidance if she needs it and the emotional energy of someone who is giving her his unflagging support and is sharing each contraction with her. The point of education for birth is that childbirth becomes not something that simply happens *to* one, but a process in which the labouring woman actively and gladly participates. And it is here that the great distinction between incidental pain – which is common to most labours – and suffering, lies. For suffering in childbirth is unnecessary and a complete anachronism nowadays. With adequate preparation beforehand and support at the time, and with the additional aid of modern obstetric analgesics or anaesthesia if necessary, no woman need suffer in labour. Instead it becomes an exciting adventure of the first magnitude, and brings with it a sense of deep satisfaction, of thrilling achievement and triumph.

The pain that occurs in most labours is not a simple result of intra-uterine pressure, and is felt only at the height of each contraction.

Many women worry that childbirth pain will prove too much for them; and that they will somehow 'give way', and reveal their true selves. The implication is that our 'real' selves are nastier than the selves which act out our days – that they form a sort of mask in front of the inherent un-

7

pleasantness of our inner natures. But we are not like this at all. Probably for most women who are bearing a child, the act of sexual intercourse is a deeply happy one, and they express themselves in love through their bodies. Coitus is an intense and over-powering experience in exactly the same sort of way as birth. One is completely caught up in the act of being, utterly committed to the moment and to the intense sensations one is tasting. A woman in labour may not look as if she has just powdered her nose or had her hair permed. But with her eyes shining and cheeks flushed, and hair damp and tangled, she is beautiful in exactly the same way as she is when she is making love. Perhaps this may be reassuring for those women who worry that labour must be the very opposite of the passionate romance that is part of the husband's and wife's physical relationship.

Nor will she behave in a way any different from her normal personality. If she quickly gets impatient or frustrated and cross, or tends to be argumentative, or if she anticipates trouble long before it occurs and 'crosses her bridges before she comes to them,' or if, on the other hand, she becomes quickly flustered and panics when things happen for which she is not prepared, these aspects of her personality will find expression also in the way she acts in labour. If she is not on very good terms with her body and thinks it rather inefficient or unlikeable, this attitude too she will carry over into her labour – and she will not really trust it to work properly.

If a woman is obsessional about housework, or about always doing the right thing, or in proving to her parents that she is not a failure, she will use labour, too, in an obsessional way, and it can easily become for her a problem in technology, a matter of management and organisation. And she may readily feel she has 'failed'. If she is dependent on her mother for instance, she may well carry over this dependence on to the midwife, who cares for her in pregnancy and labour, or her obstetrician. If she is the sort of woman who intellectualises everything and lives 'in her head', she will probably try to gain control over her labour in the same way, and may be disturbed and uneasy when she discovers that the sensations of childbirth sweep through and involve one's whole body and being, and cannot be isolated in the brain or completely controlled by the intellect.

For childbirth is not something separate and apart in which a woman's behaviour is unique. It is something which *involves characteristic responses*, even though the context of action involves a unique creative activity.

This is one reason why any one particular method of childbirth training is unlikely, ever, to suit all women, and why we need more experienced approaches to preparation and approaches which are fluid enough to adapt to different women's personality needs. Some women will always want not to 'be there' – and simply to go to sleep and wake up with a flat tummy and a pink bundle in a cot. And if this can be made a really safe method for both mother and baby – which it really is not yet – then a woman should have the right to make this decision for herself and to have her baby this way. Others want to know something of the drama of childbirth, but without the intensity of feeling which is nearly always involved in unmedicated labour; they may prefer some form of regional anaesthesia in which they are paralysed or numbed from the waist down, with spinal, caudal or epidural anaesthesia. Certainly, when those women seeking a natural birth need additional obstetric assistance these regional anaesthetics seem to be one of the best ways of allowing the woman still to participate and to share in the joy of birth.

Others feel that all the sensations of normal labour: the tug and tussle of dilatation of the uterus, the back-ache and thigh-ache and tummy-ache, the enormous stretching feelings, and the pressure of the baby's head as it is eased through the birth canal, and the slippery ecstasy as the little body is at last released and swims out into the world, limbs lashing in freedom – that all this, even though it involves discomfort and possible pain, and acute sensations which are more powerful than anything else one has ever experienced, is infinitely worth while. These are the women who say,

'Please let me try to do it myself', and who may be far too busy to be bothered with analgesic machines or injections because they are completely wrapped up in the task of giving birth, and in responding with carefulness and concentration to the stimuli coming from the uterus. Compassion and understanding on the part of those attending such women in labour consists not primarily in offering pain-relief, but in helping them do, as far as lies in their power, what they set out to do, by giving encouragement, information, and emotional support. And if interference is necessary – if delivery must be hastened for instance – this should always be explained as frankly and clearly as it can be in terms of the *baby's* and not the mother's needs. For nearly always the help which is given in a situation of this kind is really because the unborn child needs it. Most women will hand over gracefully, if need arises, if they feel that it is for their babies' sakes.

The women in these pages tell – indirectly through their stories – something of what antenatal education is all about. After reading just a few of these accounts no reader could conclude that adjustment to labour was simply a matter of breathing and blowing at the right time, or of getting the right breathing level, or having sufficient techniques of distraction at one's disposal.

There must be very few women who go through labour with a clear picture, like a diagram from an obstetrics textbook, of what is occurring in their bodies. Perhaps this is just as well. Birth is a psychosexual experience, not simply a medical event. In lovemaking, too, anatomical information gives way to fantasies about the flowing, growing, enveloping self, and perhaps the more that one can surrender to fantasies of this kind and simply *let one's body be* without directing it, the more satisfying the lovemaking activity. Some women describe their labours in terms of what happened and what they did; others draw on this extra dimension of being, the fantasies with which they were flooded and which make of the many different sensations of labour a unique pattern and a coherent whole in the imagination. I believe that the capacity for rich fantasy enriches birthing as much as it does lovemaking and that just as the vagina seems to burn, merge with another being and dissolve in sexual intercourse, so the fantasies about contractions, sensations in the birth canal and the fanning out of perineal tissues as the baby comes to birth contribute towards harmonious psychosomatic activity and the rhythmic co-ordination of breathing and body as the whole self is caught up in and focused on one imperative, urgent creative act.

For me in my own labours this has always been expressed in terms of imagery of water and its movement. I have felt gathered up on waves as contraction follows contraction with relentless power, and the birth of the baby has come as if on a tide which streamed through me.

The wave surges toward me, rises in crescendo as I am enveloped by the walls of its pressure, and then sweeps back and away, leaving my body bounded by the little space, the utter peace and content, between contractions. The uterus works mechanically like the heart, without my willing or dictating what it shall do. Its muscle fibres contract and constrict – feel as if they must grind and pulp, like a ripe peach pressed till all its juice pours out, and everything in the deep well of the pelvis is squeezed and trodden as if in a wine press.

It comes again, with controlled power. Go with it. Breathe with it, up and over. The big contractions are the *good* ones. Skim over each, brushing the wings of pain. Soar above the raging waters, the swelling wonder of creation as the womb-fruit ripens, tilts, and feels almost bursting in its strength: bigger than any other muscle in the human body, or the biceps of a champion boxer. The contraction fades, the wave washes back. Down the slope into peace, the two minutes in which my boat is beached before it must set off again into the storm.

The waves come faster, and I must go towards each with measured pace, keeping above them with my breathing. If I try to turn and run away, they will engulf me. Each one bears

11

in the tide, brings it sweeping in – the great flooding waters of birth. The gates of the body open as the baby is pressed down the arc of the birth canal, head moulded by its confines. My body is like an island fretted by waves, like a widening bay filled by the swollen tide. My cliffs and beaches are relentlessly eroded; the channels run with the foaming water, hot in its torrents. Leonardo's cataclysm was formed from waves like these, but these bear life on them, not death.

The widening bay turns warm, prickles with heat, as the tide urges toward it. My body has become a vessel from which life is poured. The child's head, like the hard bud in the middle of the peony, pushes forward between all the uncurled, spreading petals. Wait, as the flower opens. Feel the top of the baby's head with wondering fingers, the soft down of the hair, and wait for the next surge; gently ease it forward.

The pod pops. Like a seed bursting, the head slides through and slips out, sweet and smooth, eyes tightly closed, face puckered in displeasure at the world. Shoulders slither out, arms flailing, finger fronds, rib cage working, tough little thighs and heels thudding, knees churning – my child's body glowing pink – and her mouth opens in a roar as, with a tearless cry, she greets life with innocent rage.

In one sense preparation for childbirth is 'medical', of course, if only because pregnancy and labour involve physiological changes which are supervised by medical personnel, and assisted when necessary. But in another sense preparation is working through *feelings*, and concerns emotional aspects of adjustment to a phase of life, a different image of the self, and a different social role. In this sense it is not 'medical' at all, and calls on teaching and counselling skills, on techniques derived from group dynamics, and insights and research in the fields of psychology, sociology and social anthropology (personally I would add the advantages of training in acting too). Antenatal education is impoverished and drained of much that it has to offer once it is restricted to mere anatomy and physiology, relaxation drill and breathing techniques.

12

And unfortunately in many clinics throughout the country lack of time, understaffing, and lack of opportunity for further training on the part of those doing this work, mean that this is the picture often presented. Childbirth education is really a new profession, which needs a specific combination of skills, special qualities of personality, and a certain sort of previous experience, which is different again from that of the midwife or physiotherapist. At the moment, apart from the excellent and varied courses offered by the National Childbirth Trust of Great Britain,[1] taught by 'advanced' teachers and tutors from different backgrounds, most prospective antenatal teachers are having to acquire this the hard way.

The techniques used by the women whose stories are recorded here included the use of special types of breathing, neuro-muscular release, massage, postural variations and techniques of gaining increased comfort. The actual exercises they did and the responses they rehearsed beforehand are described in my book *The Experience of Childbirth*.[2] Very often they added adaptive responses of their own, and this was encouraged in my classes. I have learned a good deal from my students who have experimented in this way, and have often incorporated what they taught me into my teaching.

The basic idea behind all this is that instead of fighting one's body, trying to escape from pain, the woman in labour responds positively both with conscious and controlled respiratory patterns, which vary in terms of depth and rhythm with the phase of labour, and with the skilled relaxation which comes from an awareness of what happens to one's own body under stress and how to 'switch off' tension. It is rarely that a woman is able to do this completely with all labour contractions, but difficulty in doing so over a short series of contractions need not spell failure, since there is

1. 9 Queensborough Terrace, London W2 3TB (Tel. 01-229-9319/9310).
2. Pelican (4th edition) 1978.

always a rest period, however short, between contractions, which allows one to gain complete release of tension and to prepare for the next contraction. The use of these 'bridge periods' between contractions is most important, and especially so in the fierce storm that terminates the first stage.

Moreover everyone attending classes knows that if she feels the need there are additional pharmacological aids which she is perfectly justified in using, not 'instead' of her relaxation and breathing but in addition to them. It is not a question of 'either-or', but of the intelligent co-ordination of available techniques which seem to suit that particular labour and that particular woman.

But for a woman to feel free to do this, teaching should not merely present an ideal standard of behaviour in labour which she tries to attain. It somehow has to give a student the self-confidence and trust in her body which enables her to *incorporate* that ideal, so that it becomes part of herself and feels the natural and spontaneous way to behave. 'It seemed the obvious thing to do' . . . 'The breathing came quite easily. I didn't really have to think about it' . . . or even 'I had a shot of pethilorfan and I just went straight on breathing and relaxing, and dozing between contractions'. It is only too easy to fall short of this and to teach in a way that means that a woman goes into labour determined with all her might and main to have a labour like someone else she has heard of or read about, to 'do the exercises', to 'live up to' her teacher, or to prove something about herself. When this happens it looks as if teaching has been efficient up to a point, but has been communicated more as a series of skills than as an art. For this is the basic distinction between techniques – like piano scales or dance steps or the isolated actions of the skier practising on dry land – and an art in which all these actions are co-ordinated and synthesised into a whole, which, because it looks so easy and smooth, seems absolutely 'natural'. So there may be something to be said for 'natural childbirth' after all, a term which is now more or less taboo among childbirth educators, if not among the general public. But prepared childbirth is natural not because it teaches women that they can go out and squat in the woods with the squirrels and other wild creatures and have their babies on a pile of leaves, or that they do not need doctors and midwives or antenatal care, or that it 'shouldn't' hurt and that they have done something wrong or are unworthy if it does – but rather that the end result of careful training and of self-understanding is the co-ordinated psychophysical harmony which appears natural.

Every childbirth educator knows of women who can do all the isolated 'drills' perfectly and who are shining examples of how to do it to the rest of the class. They know too that these may well be the women who have the least happy labours and who are unable to adapt themselves to the stimuli coming to them from the uterus. It was all in the head and not in the body; this is partly the result of the whole process of the intellectualisation of a natural process which has come about through the movement for preparation for childbirth, and perhaps especially through psychoprophylaxis. Childbirth becomes more an academic exercise, or even a circus act, like a dog jumping through a burning hoop. And in this respect childbirth education is very much at the stage that sex education for marriage was in the twenties; it sometimes tends towards the dogmatic and the mechanical, and may reduce the whole process to a system of techniques.

Reading these accounts, it becomes obvious that great flexibility in method and techniques is necessary if a woman is to have the best opportunity of adjusting to any sort of labour. The one who only has a rigid training, and who is taught to do so many breaths a minute or to breathe at a special level when she is so many fingers dilated, or the one who is instructed to breathe in and out twice and then hold her breath for a count of ten with second stage contractions, *may* find that this drill suits her labour perfectly, and happens to harmonise with the type of contractions she encounters; but she may equally well discover that this blueprint somehow does not fit her particular labour, and that, however

15

disciplined her conditioned responses, she has sacrificed the chance of achieving true psychophysical co-ordination by being trained to react without thinking or feeling. It is almost as if we are sometimes frightened of the tremendous and over-powering surge of physical and emotional sensations in labour, and as if we are afraid of being 'undisciplined' and caught up in this great tumultuous sea of uterine contractions. Some sorts of antenatal drill are like learning a series of incantations, a magical device, which will ward off evil and suffering if only we repeat it consistently and mechanically. And, of course, this *may* work, and provide effective distraction from pain. 'Raising the pain threshold' the Pavlovians call it. But it is a poor second to really going 'with' one's labour and responding sensitively to the stimuli of contractions like an orchestra obeying the conductor. And occasionally, it must be admitted, these carefully learned exercises seem utterly irrelevant to a particular labour, and the woman feels she is lost on uncharted seas. This is where two things can help her: firstly the mental flexibility, self-awareness and courage to explore the possibilities of adapting and modifying techniques to suit her specific needs; and secondly, encouraging labour support which offers guidance not in terms of how labour 'ought' to be, but of how it actually is for her, and accurate information on the progress of labour.

This is where the husband who has taken the trouble to acquire the necessary knowledge, and has shared in her pre-natal preparation so that he can breathe and relax *with* her, is of untold help, and, especially in a difficult labour, can give that vital extra emotional support that permits her to get over the top of the really huge waves of contractions at the end of the first stage.

It is because childbirth cannot be reduced to a succession of exercises that support at the time of labour, and companionship and encouragement, are very important. Most women need someone there who understands what they are trying to do, and who is able to help them and in some way to share the experience with them. Many have been unable

16

to have this and have still enjoyed their labours, but the optimum emotional climate for childbirth is one in which all are working together with understanding and co-operation. So in this respect, too, childbirth is not just a series of exercises; it is also a venture in human relations. This aspect has been ignored in the past, at any rate so far as the training of the pregnant woman was concerned. She has been taught what to do, when to do it and how to recognise the various phases of her labour on the one hand, and what her attendant may do on the other, but not how to understand what is going on in the minds of her attendants, and why they may behave in a certain way, or how to communicate to them that *she* understands. This may seem to demand too much of the woman in labour, but unless it can be explored she embarks on labour with the risk of social disorientation and isolation, enduring a 'solitary confinement', while wondering what 'they' will think, what 'they' will do to her, an even – worst of all, if 'they' will 'interfere'.

What does it feel like to be a midwife when your patient is only two fingers dilated and breathing away like mad? Or when she simply seems to be working too hard and you are sorry for her? Or when it looks as if you are useless and as if she wants nothing to do with you or any help you can offer? Perhaps these things should be put into words and the ante-natal class should take time to explore human motivation and conduct in the labour ward. Because this is often the great rock on which women who have had training founder when actually in labour. It is only by putting oneself in somebody else's place, and by an act of the imagination achieving understanding, that one can be really sympathetic.

The father of the baby is usually the best person to give labour support, even though a good many start off with qualms about their role. He, more than anybody else, usually understands his wife's responses (and if he does not, maybe this is a good time to learn). He knows when tension is building up before it is apparent to anyone else, knows how to soothe and calm her, and the right words with which to give

17

her new confidence and courage. The most unlikely men are marvellous during their wives' labours – often even without previous preparation. The one who, his wife asserts, 'says "Oh horrors!" whenever the baby is mentioned,' stays with her during childbirth and cradles her in his arms as their baby is born. But it is only fair that men should be offered the opportunity of sharing to some extent in their wives' preparation, so that they understand what is happening, can anticipate what is to come, feel they have a meaningful role to play in the drama and know the precise techniques of massage, encouragement, adjustment of posture and other forms of participation so that they can be of most positive help. The couple act and react on each other during labour, and the very fact that he does not panic as soon as labour starts, wanting to rush her to the hospital immediately, or that he recognises the signs of the late first stage and is able to reassure her that she is doing well and that everything is fine, may profoundly affect her responses in labour. Nearly all the women whose stories are recorded in this book had partners who learned what to do and when to do it, and, as will be seen, frequently set about their part in childbirth with enthusiasm and great finesse.

When a man is present during labour it is most important that he has a constructive and necessary part to play and is not simply a 'hanger-on' and 'voyeur' on the scene of labour. He needs to feel that he has a definite task to perform, and should never be put in the position of being a mere observer. Indeed, to do this is, almost invariably, to waste his talents. He can easily be made to feel an intruding and non-participant onlooker who is likely to get in the way, and some forethought and planning is necessary if he is to play an active part.

One occasionally hears apocryphal stories of husbands who faint. These are the ones who feel helpless in a situation for which they are inadequately prepared, which they cannot comprehend, and which is fraught with tension and drama.

18

Denied action, all they can do is to retreat from the disturbing situation and pass out.

I remember a man who was an habitual fainter, and would pass clean out if he cut his finger and saw blood. We discussed whether he should risk being present. He decided to take a chance, and simply to walk out if he felt queasy. Should he faint, doctor and midwife agreed that they would step over his body and get on with their work. At delivery his wife needed the assistance of forceps, and he just strolled out while the baby was being delivered and was back in the room again immediately he heard his son's birth cry.

For the man – or anyone else – to be the labour 'coach' is not just a question of saying 'You're doing very well', or 'Yes, breathe like that, dear!' or 'Won't be long now' – although all these may help. It is rather a matter of sharing an experience; and this not in the sense of collapsing under the weight of a burden, or of being overwhelmingly excited with the drama of all that is going on, but of sensitively participating in the woman's hopes and accomplishment, and also of helping her to *organise* her experience so that it has meaning.

This can be very important when things start slowly, and hour after hour passes with hardly anything happening – a situation most likely to occur with first babies. This very gentle slope leads gradually to dilatation through a long-drawn-out pre-labour phase. There is nothing abnormal about such a state of affairs, but it can be very wearing for the woman in labour.

Then, too, women often lose all sense of time in advanced labour – especially in long labours. This means that they tend to become disoriented, and this in turn leads to a lowering of morale and a feeling of helplessness and hopelessness. 'I'm too tired; I can't go on. Why don't they take it away?' This state of affairs can usually be avoided if she is assisting in keeping her own log book of labour, charting her progress through these stormy seas; and when despair is imminent she

19

can be encouraged to look back and see what progress has been made: 'Contractions were coming every five minutes and lasting forty-five seconds. Now they are coming every three minutes and lasting a minute. That's an advance. Soon we shall be going into transition – the bridge between the first and second stages.'

Being with women in labour, and sharing their struggles and triumphs in this way, demands a great outpouring of energy and can be very exhausting. This is why it is really too much to ask as routine of any midwife, however dedicated to her calling and however sympathetic she is as a person. She can give calm guidance and friendship, but cannot involve herself emotionally in every labour, or she would become useless in her task, drained of energy and shattered by the multitude of moving experiences in which she was participating. To really share a labour – like sharing in dying – involves the very depths of one's being. This often happens, in spite of themselves, to those midwives who identify with a patient, and they find their eyes wet with tears as the baby makes its first world-welcoming cry, and the mother reaches out her arms for the child as it swims out of her body.

It is one reason why the partner is the obvious person to fill this role of labour companion. For him it is a significant experience in their relationship, and has an existential reality of its own. Moreover he is assenting to paternity and the responsibilities implicit in fatherhood in a tangible and real way. He is involved completely as a person who has a function which is quite different from that of the purely technical, or manipulative, or even educational.

The midwife's role is all of these, and labour also involves her as a person, but she is not committed in the same way – is not required to experience it at the same depth, unless, for some reason, this particular labour means something special to her. She is the expert, the professional; she is able to plan, calculate and assess in a way for which the couple are not usually equipped either by training or interest. The couple are wayfarers, explorers in strange territory – and because of this they are together in a different sense, if given the opportunity and support, from the midwife and mother's relationship.

I would not wish to suggest that the midwife's and the partner's functions are utterly different, because in practice they often overlap, and this harmonious overlapping is part of a good working relationship. Each contributes what they can best offer to the situation. But I do feel that the man has a role in labour which is not in any way a concession to either sentimentality or obstetric voyeurism, and which does not conflict with that of the doctor or midwife, but which is a much needed supportive and 'sharing' role.

Childbirth is part of a relationship in which the partners are committed to each other, and however dramatic and thrilling having a baby is for the couple, there is a large part of their lives together which continues, for better or worse, side by side with the pregnancy and the early days and months of parenthood. So perhaps talking about training the couple for childbirth poses only half of the problem. What they really need to learn is how to adapt themselves to changed roles *vis à vis* each other, and how to acquire the capacity of enjoying each transitional phase of their lives together. For the whole of a relationship is really a series of transitions, in which the identity of each partner is transmuted by processes involving the birth and development of children, the new stresses involved in changing relationships in the family, and the daily battles and satisfactions and pleasures of living together. Each marriage has a life of its own and is as alive and growing as a tree.

This is why classes for couples that concentrate simply upon showing the man how to rub her back or to time her breathing with a stop-watch, fall far short of the sort of help they could be offering. I remember an American obstetrician commenting that he didn't know whether there was really much point in the man helping the woman in labour, since however happy they appeared at the time, he knew of a great many cases in which the couple had separated subsequently, and he quoted the case of two couples who participated in beautiful birth films – and those marriages broke up afterwards. And as he spoke I remembered how helpless and worried one of these husbands had seemed to me, how the woman was the *prima donna* of the birth performance, and how her eyes were always on the fatherly obstetrician for guidance and support – not on her husband – of how he had tried to get her to suck ice because he had been taught to give her ice and of how she did not want it and became irritated with him. And the birth itself, with the woman straining and pushing in near desperation – rather than letting her body open up in the great unfolding mystery of sensations – as the baby presses down the birth canal and fans open the lips of the vagina and the tissues in and around it, culminated in delivery not apparently out of her body at all, but from a hole in a sheet, draped between other sheets, and over legs suspended in steel lithotomy stirrups and also draped. Somehow the whole mystery of sex had been removed from that birth by the hospital routines, and by the expert sleight of hand demonstrated by an obstetrician who acted the part almost of a magician as he deftly lifted the baby out. I remember vividly, too, that the mother, still overcome by the intensity of sensations of delivery, and by the struggle in which she had been engaged, was at first reluctant to take and hold her baby, and how she asked the nurse to give the child to her husband – and the nurse refused and insisted that *she* must take it.

In some ways the experts, with the kindliest of intentions, had seemed to me to invade that marriage and to threaten it just where it was most vulnerable; and although the couple had learned techniques of coping with labour, they, and everyone else concerned, had missed the opportunity for increased self-awareness and understanding of human needs.

However important the woman in childbirth is, and no one is denying her her central role, the point of having a baby is not simply to provide her with sensations of pleasurable achievement. The couple are doing something together which deeply affects their own partnership, the wider family of which this relationship is a part – and the great network of human relationships extending out into the present and back into time and forward into the future. Childbirth is the focal point of all these relationships; in the act of birth society is changed irrevocably. And when a woman pushes one small, screaming baby out into the world she is in that moment transforming her relationships with the father of her child, her mother and father, her other children, her sisters and brothers and grandparents and friends and neighbours – and he with his.

So this is why in this book I have welcomed the chance of recording the experiences of real people, and not only of students of a particular sort of technique of behaviour for childbirth – not simply pupils carrying out a task methodically, but individuals interacting with each other in love and need, and learning a little more about each other as they do so.

But not all labours, of course, are straightforward. And attending classes is not going to ensure that there are no obstetric abnormalities; even when labour is far from 'normal', or when a woman encounters such insuperable physiological difficulties that she needs help with a forceps delivery, vacuum extraction, or even a Caesarean section, her personal experience of labour is not simply the sum of all these events. Her own personality can, and often does, transmute each isolated event, and the whole physiological process, into something which has value in terms of her thinking and feeling about her own identity, her marriage, and what human relations and life itself mean to her. Childbirth is then part of a larger system of values, part of a pattern. And every pattern has something satisfying about it when it is contrasted with chaos, whether this is a chaotic sequence of events which we don't understand, the confusion which comes with disorientation of mental processes, or the sort of stress situation in living in which we cannot see what to do, what action we can perform, or what role we can play – like 'shell-shocked' soldiers in battle or rats in a maze which have been deliberately frustrated and confused in a laboratory situation.

Even a quick, easy labour can be chaotic in just this sort of way if the woman goes into it unprepared. And a long, difficult labour can provide its own satisfactions if the woman knows what she can do to help, and sees order and meaning instead of muddle and a bombardment of meaningless sensations.

Not all the women in these pages had their babies easily. No method of preparation could possibly ensure that labour was going to be straightforward and simple. Some women had long and arduous labours lasting several days. It is important to emphasise this because sometimes when we explain the advantages of education for childbirth the response is, 'Oh, but she would have had an easy labour anyway; she's just the type for it' . . . 'She was in her early twenties, but I'm nearly forty!' . . . 'They say I may need a Caesarean section' . . . 'My husband isn't allowed in the delivery room' . . . 'I've had this bad back ever since I was in my teens' . . . 'My blood pressure is up' or 'I have asthma, so how can I do breathing exercises!' . . . 'I had a threatened miscarriage and the doctor says I must rest' . . . 'I really can't spare the time now because I've got to get my thesis in before the baby is born' . . . 'They don't have anyone at the hospital who can remind me of my breathing so what's the point?' . . . 'There is a history of very difficult births in our family; none of us have babies easily' . . . or even 'My husband' . . . or 'My doctor . . . thinks it's better if I don't know too much, because I worry'. All these reasons for not attending classes suggest physiological or emotional problems with which childbirth education can often help a woman to cope. She may still need a Caesarean section, but she will know what to do and when to do it, is able to understand what is happening up to the point when the doctors take over, and can come out of it feeling much more a person – able to take up the responsibilities of motherhood – than the patient who is reduced, from the moment she enters hospital, to being just the body on the table. A woman may suffer severe backache in labour, but there are special techniques for helping her to control a 'backache labour' so that the baby's weight is taken off the spine as much as possible, and her morale is maintained through the long hours of dilatation. And the women who think they are not the 'type' for childbirth often find that the preparation helps them to become more flexible, less anxious or less meticulously obsessional in their need to be in command of the situation or of other people. The most unlikely women can learn how to adapt to their labours. I have had students who have started off rigid with fear: 'Quite frankly, I'm terrified of the whole thing', who reach the end of pregnancy saying, 'I can't wait for the birthday; I'm so excited.' I remember a woman who, quite apart from childbirth, was worried about generalised tension in her life, and particularly in her marriage; when it came to labour everything flowed smoothly and she found she could relax at will: 'I knew what to do all the time . . . Then I saw her come out and I put her to the breast and she sucked straight away.'

Another woman suffered from extreme mood-swings – from a state of being 'giddy and gay and darting about' and 'always in a whirl', as she said, to its opposite, when she felt life was not worth living. She was not married, had been losing blood right through early pregnancy, and smoked non-stop (not good for the baby, as the placenta cannot sieve off the poisonous chemicals in tobacco smoke). No one in her family thought that she would ever have the self-discipline or concentration to practise exercises, or the self-control not to go to pieces in labour. But she managed beautifully. It seemed, in fact, the first thing she had done all by herself, and at which she had been really successful. 'It was *very* interesting,' she told me. 'But it would have been terrible if you didn't know about it. As it was I felt I knew everything that was happening, and the breathing was *marvellous*. I didn't have much pain. In fact, I wandered round most of the first stage – no problems that way at all, and it was all ever so easy to deal with.' It was only afterwards, when she

25

reached the end of her story, that I learned that the baby did not come down the birth canal in the correct position, and that she was delivered by forceps. To her this was purely incidental compared to the happiness and sense of achievement she felt about having co-operated in the birth of her baby.

So the women who form the *dramatis personae* of these pages are no paragons, either. My own antenatal students and other women who had read my book *The Experience of Childbirth*,[1] from whose reports these are selected – simply on the grounds that here were women who could express what they felt – do not, of course, present a random sample. They are not possessed of superhuman powers of endurance, and they vary in the degree to which they perceive and suffer pain, the books they read, the jobs they do, their social class, cultural background, intelligence, schooling, and in the way in which they want their babies and love their husbands. Some of them had encountered emotional problems which made them doubt their ability to give birth naturally or to be a good mother, or wife, or even to go on living positively, with anything to contribute to life. These had often sought me out because they knew that problems interested me and I was not keen on simply teaching exercises and explaining physiological processes. Often in the accompanying letter from their doctors there were remarks about Mrs S. not being 'able to relax', or being 'tense', 'apprehensive', 'fearful' or 'depressed'. So in a way we were not starting off with the highest of hopes, and we knew it might be a hard, long struggle. Some had not really wanted a baby at all, or at any rate, not then; a few were unmarried, and some had contemplated having an abortion and felt guilty, ashamed, or worried about possible effects on the baby. One or two had tried to finish their own lives. Others had had psychiatric treatment and had been in mental hospitals, sometimes for years. Some were not happily married: some had been through a stage of their lives when they were addicted to

1. Pelican (4th edition) 1978.

26

drugs. And apart from all these difficulties, some women knew that their own mothers had suffered terribly in childbirth, that there was a history of difficult birth in their families, or had endured sexual trauma themselves which was interfering with their pleasure in intercourse and in their own bodies. And there was a wide range of physical illnesses, including severe asthma, pelvic injury and, of course, the raised blood pressure, excessive weight gain, oedema of the tissues and albumin in the urine which presents the classic picture of the toxaemias of pregnancy. And in age they range from seventeen to forty-two.

This must sound as if we are an odd lot in classes! But if one looks behind the faces in any crowd and sees the lines of worry and the pattern of muscle tensions which betray anxiety, it becomes clear that even the most ordinary looking people can be living in private turmoil, and that none of us are without problems. It is only that we choose to operate as if we were all fairly stable and contented individuals simply because to do anything else, to give time to listen, or to reach out with sympathetic understanding, would prove too time-consuming, exhausting and disturbing. In ordinary situations of living we cannot afford to 'take the lid off'; we agree implicitly on standards of social behaviour which inhibit the expression of our deepest fears or our worst doubts. It seems to me, however, that antenatal counselling provides opportunity for coming face to face with some of these problems, and that this may often be necessary before the woman can go forward happily into her labour and into motherhood. In my own teaching course I see each woman privately, usually with her husband too, at least once for a consultation which can last anything from one hour to a whole evening, and we use the group not only for doing exercises and imparting information, but also for discussion of the emotional aspects of childbearing.

Emotions in pregnancy and birth are not inconvenient symptoms which need to be nullified by drugs, or by escape from sensation. The emotional changes of pregnancy can often provide clues as to what needs to be done and the necessary adjustments in interpersonal relationships. As J. A. C. Brown says,[1] 'Freud devised a means of diagnosing man's troubles, not of suppressing them, and the emotions we are so desirous of suppressing are the mental equivalents of body symptoms which may give warning that all is not well . . . The very real danger today is that neuroses may cease to be dealt with by psychological methods based on understanding at all, and that with new pharmacological and medical or surgical methods we shall be 'cured' by being made insensible to conflicts rather than facing up to them and trying to understand what is wrong with our way of life. Instead of realising that there are circumstances which justify attitudes of guilt, remorse, shame, anxiety, or injustice, we shall treat them as inconvenient 'symptoms' to be dispelled by a tranquilliser or thymoleptic drug.'

Some women worry, on being told that they are 'elderly primips' or that they need a 'trial' of labour, and perhaps Caesarean section, that things are going terribly wrong, and even perhaps that there is no point in preparing themselves for labour, as it is all going to be taken out of their hands anyway. Nothing could be further from the truth and there are several accounts of labour from women having their first babies in their late thirties in the pages that follow. If there are special problems, or if a woman falls into a 'high risk' category, there is all the *more* reason why she should learn how she can help herself to maintain good health, correct posture, and a positive emotional attitude during pregnancy, to use available techniques in response to the stimuli of the contracting uterus and the discomforts of 'backache labour', and also learn the ways in which she can best co-operate with her attendants to take advantage of the assistance which can be offered both to her and the baby. Ignorance and noncomprehension will not help her; understanding can. A good obstetrician works much better when

1. *Freud and the Post-Freudians* (Penguin, 1969).

28

he or she can work *with* the mother and not just *on* her.

This is why so many doctors emphasise the importance of the relationship between themselves and their patients. They often call it one of 'trust'; it need not be a blind leaning on the obstetrician's superior wisdom. It can mean the woman's intelligent participation, in which she works as part of a team, and in which she is playing not the role of a child, but of an adult participating in a vital life process.

I remember being with one of my students when she was having a vacuum extraction. This was necessary because of transverse arrest as the baby descended the birth canal. She was allergic to various drugs, and in order not to spark off an allergic reaction it was decided to use general anaesthesia for the few moments of delivery during which the vacuum extractor would bring the baby right down on to the perineum, rotating the head in the process, and then suck it out from the mother's body. The obstetrician turned to me and remarked that he had never used the vacuum extractor with an unconscious woman before, that it was inconvenient for him, and not half as easy; he always relied on the informed participation of the mother, and worked *with* her to get the baby born. When a contraction came she told him, and she held her breath and pushed the baby deep into the birth canal, releasing her pelvic floor muscles as she did so, while at the same time he drew the baby forward with suction. In this case he did a beautiful delivery – and the mother woke up to a gorgeous baby. But he made it quite clear that his preference for having the mother's active co-operation was nothing to do with the benefits for the mother's psyche, but was simply a matter of making his task much easier.

Those readers who are expecting to be delivered at home can look forward to the comfort of familiar surroundings and the concentrated personal attention of a midwife who will be with them throughout active labour. This can be a tremendous advantage in helping birth to take place as part of the natural process of living, and not as something strange and rather alarming. We are beginning to rediscover some of the benefits of home delivery – which with the development of modern, hospital-backed maternity services are so lightly cast aside – for both mother and baby, and certainly for the father and for any other children.[1,2] In Britain specially equipped personnel are on hand to speed to the woman's home if necessary. These 'Flying Squads' based on large hospitals are highly efficient, quick, and, in spite of their name, undramatic. They bring with them general anaesthesia and can perform certain obstetric operations in the bedroom, with but slight disturbance to the household, and stay till all is well. They are used particularly when the woman is bleeding heavily in the third stage of labour, usually when the placenta has not separated properly.

Whereas hospital confinement cannot be taken as a criterion of care, antenatal care *can*. One study revealed that when women had no antenatal care at all, the perinatal mortality rate (that is the death of the baby at birth or within the first week after) shot up by an incredible 500%.[3] Childbirth education only makes sense if it is partnered by good antenatal care. It is really only because childbirth is now so safe – and this safety is closely associated with all the laborious routines of the antenatal clinic – that women can afford to think about the less tangible aspects of having a baby, about their feelings, for instance, and their own roles in labour.

1. *The Place of Birth*, ed. Sheila Kitzinger and John A. Davis (O.U.P., 1978).
2. *Birth at Home*, Sheila Kitzinger (O.U.P., 1979).
3. *In the Beginning*, Richard Shegog, *et al*. (O.U.P., 1970).

CHAPTER TWO

PREGNANCY AND THE COUPLE'S RELATIONSHIP

Most of the women in these pages had their husbands with them during labour, the majority of whom were present at delivery too. This was not just an isolated incident in their lives, however, nor was it simply a matter of learning what to do and what was happening in childbirth. The labour is part of a continuum which includes the whole experience of child-bearing, becoming parents, and growing as parents.

For both man and woman the nine months' waiting are in many ways a time of preparation. Not only is the woman's body altering but subtle changes are often taking place in her outlook on life, the way she feels about herself and her body, and frequently even in her interests too. She may have been the last woman ever to peep in a pram as it stood waiting outside a shop, but now everything about babies can become almost enthralling. This is more than many a husband can stand, and he may begin to wonder what has come over the woman he knew, who was sensible and interested in the same sort of things as he was. She may be more easily moved to laughter and tears, more quickly upset by each petty quarrel or what she sees as lack of interest on his part, more snappily critical of her mother or mother-in-law. She may talk so much about the baby or her exercises that he is bored stiff with the whole business and only wishes it was over with. Or she may be happier and more relaxed and suddenly more sure of herself and confident in the idea of motherhood, as if at last she has a chance of being something and doing something she always wanted to be and do. So much so that the husband can feel that she no longer needs him in the same

31

way, and that their marriage has changed – and not for the better.

Nights may be far from peaceful because the expectant mother is at her most vulnerable in the hours of darkness, and may be unable to drop off to sleep, or may wake up and worry in the early hours of the morning. Sometimes she has had bad or disturbing dreams, which she may not remember, and they can amount to nightmares. One of these women, for instance, had reported dreams of being strapped to a delivery table with the baby separate from her in a glass bottle. Once the baby is kicking vigorously this alone may be enough to cause disturbed sleep, and if the bed is small (or the husband is large) neither husband nor wife may be getting enough sleep. This is the time in the marriage to buy a larger bed if funds will run to it, or to push two beds together if the room is large enough, perhaps a double and a single side by side. (They can always visit each other.)

Sessions at the hospital or surgery may be matters of great moment, and she seems to go on endlessly about what 'they' said and what 'they' did to her, and whether Peggy, who is due at the same time, is bigger or about the same size as she is, and whether she is putting on too much weight. Some of the women in these pages commented to me, at one time or another, 'I come back from the clinic and I just burst into tears!' I remember one saying in despair, 'They reduce me to *nothing*'. For the husband this is another world, and he may find it difficult to understand why she should get 'worked up' because the doctor or a nurse said something to her which she interprets as meaning that everything is not going well, the baby is not big enough, or she is not big enough, or she is too small, or her perineum is tight.

And in advanced pregnancy she carries on this extra-ordinary two-way conversation with the world outside her – other people, things she can see and hear and communicate with in the outside world – and with the baby inside her, moving deep in her body. This can be uncanny for a man and he may find it a disturbing element in their relationship –

especially when they make love and he feels this sudden other life. More than one of these husbands found intercourse distasteful because of this. Women themselves interpret these stirrings of life in many different ways too; some finding them pleasurable, even exciting, others hating them and conceptualising the baby as an invader of their bodies, or as a parasite growing inside.

And ahead of her lies the labour. It is unfashionable today for a woman to admit to fear of childbirth. When I meet women for their private consultations at the start of the antenatal course I find that even the most obviously worried, nervous woman will try to avoid such an admission, as if there were something shameful and disgraceful about it. There is a general attitude that, now that women can learn so much more about their bodies, there is no reason why they should be alarmed, and that to be so is silly and irrational.

Yet childbirth is an utterly new experience and one which, however commonly it is enacted every minute of every day all over the world, involves almost incredible physiological processes when one actually imagines it happening to one's own body. What is more natural than some misgivings about being launched into the unknown? In any similar situation we should also – and quite reasonably – be apprehensive. Any man, however strong and 'masculine' his sense of identity, might feel apprehensive when confronted by such an experience, and anxiety of this kind is not a 'feminine characteristic'.

For such anxiety alerts and signals attention. It can be used constructively to initiate a positive course of action, just as a woman cooks ahead when she is expecting a number of weekend guests or as the sailor reefs her sails and presents less canvas to the wind when a gale is approaching. One need not be helplessly at the mercy of events. There is no need to suffer processes either outside or inside. As Charles Rycroft says, in *Anxiety and Neurosis*,[1] 'The capacity to be

1. Penguin (1970).

33

anxious is a biological function necessary for survival.' Anxiety can serve the function of mobilising energy, marshalling forces to meet a challenge.

This may be why a woman who is obviously anxious and 'nervy', and who cannot relax during early pregnancy, may actually cope quite well in labour, and surprise both herself and her attendants.

So some anxiety is a normal occurrence in pregnancy, but the subjects on which it is focused vary, and it would be wrong to presuppose that all anxiety associated with childbearing is linked with fear of pain in labour. Even if the woman *says* that is what worries her (and this is the sort of thing which seems a satisfying sort of answer in a questionnaire for instance) she does so in an interview often only because she feels she has been driven into a corner and has to say *something*.

This sort of problem can probably never be understood by tackling it as if anxiety could be put into clearly defined categories of 'fear of pain', 'that something will happen to the baby', or of death. Because women sometimes deceive even themselves over what they are distressed about, let us examine more closely the vague feelings of threat – often very diffuse – which are frequently associated with this venture into the unknown.

There is often, of course, fear of pain which is more than she is able to bear. But the vital element in this may be the dread that she will break down, 'make a fool' of herself, cry out or swear, fling off her clothes, or say irrational things, and that thus an uglier but truer self will be revealed. To do this is to put herself in a shameful situation – one which she deserves. It is met by social scorn and ridicule. It is this humiliating aspect of how a woman sees childbirth that forms the kernel of the anxiety. Physically exposed, emotionally exposed, subjugated by the act of birth, and under the critical eye of nurses and doctors (or this is how she sees it) she will be humiliated by her own self-revelation and by a train of actions over which she has no control.

The woman who feels like this does not only suffer from such a dread of exposure in labour. This is part of a much larger and more general fear that her defences will collapse. It is useless for a woman to face up to this problem as if it existed solely in the context of childbirth. It may be very important for her, and an opportunity for increased self-awareness and maturation when she can say to herself, 'Yes, I feel I have to keep all the barriers up tight because I might so easily overstep the mark. I have all this nastiness and ugliness inside me and I'm afraid of it bursting out.' It is then that education for childbirth can help her to see that being a woman, having a baby, and experiencing the sweep of emotions she has then and in the love relationship of which the conception and birth is an integral part, is fascinating and beautiful. The preparation for birth is touching on the wider sphere of her whole psychological life, and not only on the fact of pushing a baby out into the world.

Another vortex of anxiety centres round a fear of disintegration – the very loss of the self. This may also be connected with feeling that childbirth is a humiliating process, but there is an additional element – that one must not lose control, take any form of drug or accept any assistance from medical or nursing staff lest one's personality dissolves. This sounds fairly improbable – even amusing – on paper, but in fact it is a terrifying notion. Ibsen, in *Peer Gynt*, wrote about the man who was nothing, and when onion skin after onion skin was peeled away to try to find the essential man underneath, there was nothing there.

The anxious woman clings on to her threatened identity, and sees the midwife's touch and the doctor's examination as ways in which she is stripped of her 'self'. She may fight all along the way, rigid and resisting, bound by muscle tensions with which she seeks unconsciously to define and frame her body, her physical identity, and trace the boundaries of her body image. The *ego* grows out of a baby's gradually increasing physical awareness – his sensory groping to know the world around, and each reaching-out movement, whether

of tongue, lips and gums, or of eye, or hand or hearing, results in a defining of self and its limits, as well as knowledge
of the surrounding environment. At first the new baby cannot
know where he leaves off and the mother begins. But bit by
bit the concept of self and otherness is built up, and this is
based on and expressed through the body. Yet the body we
visualise ourselves as having may be rather different from the
body that other people see, especially in times of rapid
change, as in pregnancy. Pregnancy and birth, like puberty,
the menopause, old age, and dying, involve physical metamorphosis, a period of transition between one state of physiological being and another. They all form transitional crises,
bridges also between different concepts of the self and even
different roles in society.

If a woman has never experienced a sense of *completeness*
and firmly established identity – of being herself and content
in herself – pregnancy may prove an acute threat to her self-
image in just this way. The satisfying defined boundaries of
the self are difficult to achieve unless the individual has had
some experience of success – of having achieved something
(whether it is school work, or pottery, or horse-riding, or
dancing, cookery, or simply being a person in her own right),
and this is gradually constructed during childhood in person-
to-person relationships with those we love or esteem. (To
lack this is to suffer denial of one of the basic rights of a child
as he reaches out to attempt to master his universe.) Everyone needs this experience of success, initially in the eyes of
loved parents. When a woman has never felt secure in this
she embarks on the challenge of childbearing feeling that she
is bound to fail and 'let people down', and under great stress
she may feel that her identity will disappear like a drop of
water evaporating in the air. In its most severe form this sense
of threatened identity is psychopathological and can require
concentrated and prolonged therapy. On the other hand this
is an experience which at times in our lives we probably all
share. In pregnancy a woman is emotionally fluid and capable of enormous change and maturation, and there is not

only the challenge of childbirth but also, because of this very flexibility, the opportunity of growing-up.

The pregnant woman is usually part of a loving relationship, side by side with the father of her child, who can help this process by in some ways taking the place of the parents. For in many ways we seek from our partners the things we wanted from our parents – some of which we may have been denied. Often a woman recreates her idea of a loving father in the man she loves – not perhaps anything like the man who was actually her father. When she talks about her marriage and about her mother's and father's relationship, or her idea of it, she often draws comparisons: 'Dad was like that too.' Or she may have determined to pick a different sort of man and has deliberately chosen a husband who was in every way the opposite of her idea of her father, and her expectations of his behaviour will be determined by her conceptualisation of this rejected image of manhood. It is rather like a stencil from which one can do a tracing either on the inside or the outside of the figure.

Many a man finds himself caught up in this drama of character delineation without knowing why or what is happening, and is bewildered by his wife's criticisms of him, the things which irritate her, and the accusations she makes in a quarrel. He has yet to learn that they are not just a 'couple' in isolation, but part of a family, whether they like it or not. That family extends back in time through the generations, frequently repeating its plots and its problems, but in different settings, as well as stretching its branches out in the present and future. When she reacts in this unreasonable way to something he says or does, she is reacting not just to him, but to her father and mother, and this echoes in some aspects the relationship that *they* had with their parents, and so on.

All this can come to a head during a pregnancy in which the woman is suffering from anxiety. So often the problems are explained away as being due to her 'unstable emotional state': 'She is a bit weepy,' they say, 'because she's expecting the baby.' 'Don't take any notice. Take her out and she'll forget about it', so evading the issue, and the opportunity. It is then too that fear of childbirth may be produced as the excuse for the upset. But this is not the point, for the crisis of giving birth is the occasion and symbol for many things which really describe a state of personal identity in relation to others.

One of the signs that a woman needs more help than she is getting is if she is not sleeping well – either failure to get to sleep or waking in the night. We have seen that this may be because the baby is so active, or may be because she has to keep on emptying her bladder, or has indigestion or heartburn. Not being able to sleep is often explained by reference to these physiological causes. But I have noticed that when a woman has the opportunity to talk she often begins to remember disturbing dreams, and worries that have occupied her mind at two or three in the morning when she lay awake in the darkness. In quiet and unhurried discussion she is then often able to face up to some of her fears. But to do this somebody must be prepared to listen without judgement, or slick interpretation, or trying to sweep problems away as if they did not matter with a 'Don't worry, everything will be all right', simply offering friendship and understanding companionship. This is where a partner who can give time to listen can help most constructively, and where the childbirth educator who provides more than training classes can also help.

Sometimes women just cannot express in words what they feel. Occasionally they can help themselves best by painting, drawing or modelling clay – somehow giving their fears objective reality, bringing them outside themselves. The woman who had the terrifying dreams about delivery did this, and produced a vivid and disturbing painting. I often use her paintings when we talk in class about fear of pregnancy, and I told her how helpful they were. 'It helped me to do the paintings,' she said, 'but what helps me most of all is the thought that they are of some use, and that what I went through isn't just wasted.' The creation of an acceptable channel for the expression of emotion is a logical method of handling stress, and very much better than bottling it all up and pretending that everything is all right if it is not.

The emotions which are often worked through can put extra stress on a relationship, so that it looks as if the baby, far from cementing the partnership, could actually destroy it. The child can then become the scapegoat. But it really starts when the couple can no longer find a basis for shared experience. From then on the nappies hanging to dry, the baby's demands, his preoccupation with what is going on in the office, his remarks about her mother and her friends, and hers about his friends, his untidiness or her cooking, the way he behaves with other women, even the television programme each wants to watch, can produce sparks to feed the flames of resentment, jealousy, and even hate.

Or the birth of a baby can be a growing-point in a relationship. The couples in this book had taken time to prepare themselves not only for childbirth, but also for parenthood, and some of them remarked that they understood each other better now. For most – whether they were together at delivery or not – the birth of their babies had been a shared experience – not an isolated one, neither an end in itself, nor just a 'beautiful happening', but part of a growing relationship in which each became more vividly aware of the other's needs and the other's reality.

Childbirth is not merely a clinical event. It can be a peak experience in a woman's psychosexual life, one full of challenge and excitement, deep satisfaction and joy, which she recollects with delight many years afterwards. Pregnancy and birth are also part of a developmental process in a couple's relationship, which may bring difficulties and even crises too, but if met with understanding can nourish that relationship. When this happens it is not only a baby who is delivered, but a family that is born.

PART II

THE BIRTHS

These labour reports were usually written within a couple of days of the birth, and sometimes after just a few hours. Where husbands and wives both wrote accounts they did so without consultation. I have left them more or less just as they were written, except that occasionally I have edited one to make the sense clearer, and a few long ones had to be abbreviated. I have not included – and this would have required too many exclamation marks – the things that people said over the phone; the husband frequently rings me up very soon after the baby is born to let me know what happened, and that account is usually interspersed with . . . 'Fantastic! . . . Wonderful! . . . Absolutely marvellous'. If some readers miss the superlatives in some accounts, and find them a bit flat after what they had expected, this may be partly because the writers were not the sort of people to express themselves in this way, and partly because, having already talked to me over the phone, they knew that I realised how thrilling the whole thing had been, and are now concerned to get down to accurate and detailed description of just what happened.

In my classes for preparing for birth mothers who have just had their babies usually come back, with the newborn child, and often with their partners too – to tell the other women about their labours, so that they can ask them searching questions, and get the details at first hand, and not through me. I think this is important, because I might somehow miss the things that really mattered for that particular woman, and might even be tempted to gloss over experiences which are much better brought to light – the tedium of many a labour, feelings of irritation, tiredness, worry, anti-climax afterwards. It is also a good idea for the class to discuss with

43

the mother herself how she is coping with the new baby, and then the whole idea of 'mothercraft' takes on a new reality. I remember domestic science lessons at school which seemed to have no relation at all to what one actually did in a house and how one fed a family. Well, some mothercraft lessons are a bit like that! Much better to discuss it all in terms of real life, the time your husband gets home from work and the stresses and strains of the relations, people giving good advice, a baby who wants to be bounced up and down all evening, the problem of getting enough sleep, how to manage the cooking and the nappies, and how on earth you are going to fit in making the bed, clearing the draining board, and unstopping the sink of tea leaves!

In the accounts of birth which women give the other mothers in the class I often notice a sense of adventure and fun which may be missed from the written report. On the other hand it does not seem quite fair to take it down verbatim, so I have stuck to what they have written, simply because they have had more time to consider carefully and assess what they say.

All the names have been altered, and any other details which would make recognition easy.

To start with, let us look at two 'log books', so that readers unfamiliar with the patterns of normal labour can get their bearings.

In the first example the woman was probably dilating soon after 6 p.m. till midnight, with contractions increasing from about five minute to two minute intervals. This means that during this time the cervix, or neck of the uterus, which hangs down like the neck of a bottle in the vagina, was gradually opening up until the uterus and vagina became one uninterrupted channel through which the baby could be pressed.

The contractions lasted about half a minute at first probably, and later just over a minute. When the uterus contracted, the longitudinal fibres running from top to bottom of what is virtually a hollow bag of muscle, were pulled up, shortened and thickened, and this had the effect of progressively opening the circular fibres around the cervix. This is what a contraction basically consists of.

Towards the end of the stage of dilatation – the *first stage* – when the cervix is almost open, like a tight polo-neck sweater through which the crown of the baby's head is being firmly pressed, the stretching of muscle fibres tends to be painful, and this is often called a 'pain period' of labour. Contractions are usually felt at their strongest and are most difficult to handle then.

At about 11.30 p.m. this woman entered the *transition phase* with contractions coming one on top of another, more or less unpredictably and sometimes with two peaks. A lip of the cervix is still gripping the baby's head – the *anterior lip* to which the mother refers. The urge to push the baby out frequently starts during this phase, and involves extreme rectal pressure and a catch in the breath. But it is better to avoid pushing till the cervix is *fully dilated* to save strain on the tissues.

Then, at midnight, she went into the *second stage*. That is, the cervix was completely open, an oval about the size of the palm of a man's large hand, including the thumb joint. This is the stage of expulsion, when the woman wants, sometimes very urgently, to bear down, holding her breath and opening up below. Once the head is *on the perineum*, the tissues between and around the anus and vagina gradually fan out with the steady pressure from above downwards, and the top of the baby's head can be seen in the vagina, appearing and then seeming to recede between contractions as the lips of the vagina close over it again. Delivery is preceded by the *crowning* of the baby's head. This was happening as the Sister said, 'Pant now'. The *occiput* comes to the opening but does not slip back again between contractions. From this point on the mother breathes out the baby unless instructed to otherwise, letting the uterus do its expulsive work alone. In this case the Sister told the mother to pant again, and then a third time as she unlooped the cord round the baby's shoulders so that they could slide round to be delivered. The baby then slipped out and delivery was completed. In this case the second stage lasted half an hour, from the time when the mother started pushing till the delivery.

In the *third stage* the uterus goes on contracting, and because the placenta, or after-birth, cannot contract, it is peeled off the lining of the uterus and slips into the vagina. The mother feels a contraction and gives a push – or several pushes – and the placenta is delivered. This mother did this ten minutes after the baby was born, which is about the usual length of time. That marks the end of labour.

REALLY A TEAM

Irregular contractions from 6.00 p.m. on.

9.15 p.m. Came into hospital. Diaphragmatic-costal breathing. Enema, Bath and Bed. (1)

9.45 p.m. Contractions much stronger, at five minute intervals or less. Strong alternate with weaker. Middle chest breathing.

10.15 p.m. Contractions every two minutes, very strong, but no discomfort except sensation of head pushing on rectum very strong. Breathing up to shallow chest.

10.45 p.m. Sister B. made her first internal examination. Three fingers dilated. Head so low she had to feel round it.

11.00 p.m. Sister said, 'Which first – phone your husband, pethidine – or a hot water bottle?' I said, 'Phone Robin!'

11.15 p.m. Pethidine and hot water bottle.

11.20 p.m. I suggested I should go to labour ward while I could still walk there. Up on to bed with three pillows and one under knees. Very comfy.

11.30 p.m. Robin arrived. Contractions now very strong and almost continuous, but manageable. Vigorous movements of baby.

Robin moistened my lips with flannel. (2)

11.45–12.00 p.m. 2nd examination – slight anterior lip.

12.00 p.m. Need to bear down – did mouth-centred breathing for first two contractions. Then feet up on Sister and nurse on each side and Robin propped me behind, two pushing contractions – found it hard to get rhythm. Then Sister said, 'Pant now . . . and again!' and shielded perineum as head born.

12.25 a.m. Asked to pant again, as cord round shoulders which didn't rotate, and Sister had to unloop it.

12.30 a.m. Simon arrived! Sister sucked mucus out and he cried in two minutes, and then I held him. Robin's first words: 'It's a boy! Well done, darling!'

12.40 a.m. Had to push hard to make placenta come away. Simon weighed 8 lb 9 oz. He feeds like a little pig. He's a dear little thing and we are thrilled with him.

I was very lucky in my midwife here – very helpful and 'with it', and the atmosphere in the labour ward when Robin arrived was really that of a team, as she included him in everything – altogether an enjoyable experience.

Notes

1. This is 'prepping'. The mother's pubic hair is also usually partially shaved. Sometimes a suppository is given instead of the enema.

2. When breathing in and out through parted lips, the mother's mouth tends to get very dry. Women therefore take sips of water, suck ice chips in between contractions, suck on a face flannel or sponge, and may put some sort of gloss stick on their lips.

A LONG LABOUR WITH THE BABY IN AN AWKWARD POSITION

Sue was still in her teens, very nervous, dependent on her mother, and not at all sure how much she could depend on her husband, or whether, in fact, she really wanted to.

I had my first show on Monday at 11.30 a.m., mild at first, increasing over the next two days to a thicker and darker substance in colour. The contractions started at 2.00 a.m. Thursday and felt like wind, smooth and gold in colour, if that sounds possible! They came every quarter of an hour for the next two hours, and my husband then made me some brandy and hot milk and I slept till 9.00 a.m. I had a cup of tea and a warm bath, and then the contractions seemed to stop. I then phoned Mrs K. and she suggested that I went for a brisk mile walk, which I did. After lunch, which consisted of soup and cheese and biscuits, the contractions started again at quarter hourly intervals, time 3.00 p.m. I had another hot milk and brandy and slept from 4.00 p.m. to 5.30 p.m. and when I woke up they were becoming far more severe, requiring deep breathing.

At 10.30 p.m. I phone Mrs K. and they were coming about every six minutes, so she suggested that I went to bed and tried to sleep to get some reserve energy. I started logging my contractions, and they seemed to last, on an average, 45 seconds every five minutes. I phoned Mrs K. once again about 3.30 a.m. and we all decided to leave for the G.P. Unit.

My husband and I arrived about 4.00 a.m. and I was looked after by a midwife, Miss F. who then took my pulse,

49

temperature and blood pressure, shaved me and gave me an enema, which I found most distasteful! All this took quite some time, and at 7.15 a.m. Friday I was in bed in the admissions room, still having contractions lasting half a minute every five minutes. Coping well with deep and shallow breathing. Talkative and gay.

8.00 a.m. Show and waters leaking. Vomited.

8.15 a.m. Contractions every four minutes.

8.40 a.m. Suggestion of pressure at base of spine, increasing at end of contractions. Well relaxed during contractions. Increasing irritability. Dozing between contractions.

9.00 a.m. 1 : 3 Fed up!

9.20 a.m. Contractions now last one minute. Happy and joking between contractions, but a bit weary.

9.25 a.m. 1 : 2 Midwife 'She's super, isn't she?'

9.55 a.m. First examination P.V. (1) Seven centimetres. Hiccups.

10.10 a.m. Contractions sometimes more frequent. My husband heard baby's heartbeats at midwife's suggestion. My mother visited between contractions.

10.15 a.m. Contractions settled into very smooth, mild regular rhythm. I handled them perfectly, dropping straight off to sleep between them. I was doing 'wave' breathing, culminating in mouth-centred breathing, and blew out at the end of each contraction.

10.50 a.m. I felt myself beginning to open up. I said, 'They are really beginning to hurt now', but the next one did not. They tended to alternate in power.

11.10 a.m. Feeling cold. Said, 'Oh God, when is it going to end? I'd like to go home', and got cross.

12 midday. Rather shivery. Contractions were less intense than two hours ago.

1.00 p.m. Lip. The doctor examined me and found an oblique occiput.

1.15 p.m. I said 'Help me' at the end of a contraction with the urge to push. Odd feeling. The transition was just beginning.

1.40 p.m. Urge to bear down definite. But with next contraction the urge not there.

1.45 p.m. Vomited slightly.

2.10 p.m. Very relaxed and drowsy.

2.35 p.m. Legs cold.

2.45 p.m. A good deal more waters came.

3.00 p.m. Second stage. Starting to bear down.

3.30 p.m. Delivery room.

4.00 p.m. Contractions seemed to slow down.

4.15 p.m. Tremendous urges to push and pushed strongly.

4.54 p.m. Delivery, and it's a boy, Crispin, 7 lb 5 oz. Absolutely amazing!

Once I had accepted the fact that it wasn't going to be born
through my back passage, I really put all my strength into
three bearings down to one contraction, and later managed
four. The birth of the head was unbelievable and caused very
little pain indeed. Marvellous, no episiotomy, (2) and careful
creaming of the labia with Hibitane helped this I'm sure. It
was a completely safe and wonderful experience. The coming
away of the placenta was most enjoyable, so warm, and rich
in colour.

Only on a couple of occasions did I feel like throwing in
the towel and forgetting the whole issue, but I'm sure it was
mainly due to fatigue and the length of labour. I had a
wonderful team helping me, Mrs K., my husband and the
midwife, and I owe this marvellous experience to each one
individually.

Notes

1. *per vaginam* – through the vagina. Earlier ones are often
   done through the rectum.
2. This is an incision made (with scissors) in the perineum to
   speed up the delivery of the head and/or to prevent the
   mother tearing. It is done either under local anaesthesia
   or at the height of a contraction when pressure from above
   numbs the tissues. Women often do not feel it, or even do

not know it has been done at the time, but it can be un-comfortable afterwards (hot and prickling) as the tissues heal and the hair starts growing again. The suturing after delivery can be a bore, as it may take a long time and seem an awful anti-climax.

THE FATHER DELIVERS THE BABY

This couple lived in a caravan.

Labour started at 2.00 a.m. and the midwife examined me at 4.30 a.m. when contractions were every four minutes, but found I was only one finger dilated. She returned home and we returned to bed to rest, the contractions having more or less petered out.

At 6 a.m. they returned every five minutes and got stronger quickly, and about 6.50 a.m. they started coming every two minutes, but only lasted between 40 seconds and a minute. Just after 7.00 a.m. I lay down again and the waters broke. My husband drove off to phone the midwife. He was gone about seven minutes, and while he was away, I realised the baby was imminent and thought I should have to deliver it myself. Between contractions I banked myself up with more pillows, positioned myself so that I could see the birth outlet in a mirror I had on the wall, and fed myself sips of a glucose drink as my mouth was dry. I did absolutely no pushing but did shallow breathing and blowing out, (1) and then just the panting, firstly to slow things down as much as possible, and then, when I could see the head, to prevent a tear.

My husband returned at this point, and with the next contraction the head crowned. He supported the head as it was born, and then lifted the baby after the shoulders had been born. The baby cried and my husband turned him over to drain any mucus, disentangled him from the cord and wrapped him in a towel and put him on the bed between my legs.

The midwife arrived some five or ten minutes later. We

are both very proud of ourselves and each other, and very glad of our training.

Notes

1. This blowing out lifts the diaphragm so that the expulsive action of the uterus is minimal.

AN INDUCED LABOUR

The following account describes an arduous labour which was complicated by the fact that monitors and drips meant that the woman had to stay in bed more or less immobilised. Her baby was in a posterior position (facing her front instead of her back) and might have been encouraged to turn by her standing upright, walking, moving into positions which she found more comfortable, and letting gravity help. Note that when she did turn over on her side to have the epidural the baby rotated into the correct position, but at this point she was anaesthetised and could not feel the contractions, with the result that she was delivered by forceps anyway.

Meg showed signs of diabetes in the last months and had occasional high blood pressure readings. Her dates were in question as she had conceived immediately after stopping the Pill and she was 31. She went into hospital overnight.

I was woken at 6.00 by the other girls chatting and the baby doing her early morning exercises. I was examined by Sister at 7.45 and the suppositories were inserted – relaxation worked perfectly – then sat writing this report and drinking tea, waiting for them to work. They did, but there was no drama. Then I had a long luxurious, bubbly bath. I oiled my tummy for the last time, out of habit more than need (a good habit though – I haven't any stretch marks), did my face, tied back my hair with the red ribbon Grigor had bought me specially for the occasion, and had breakfast. I had a second cup of tea too, thinking I might as well really need that hourly bed-pan!

Then I waited, writing and looking out at the mist, feeling sorry for G. having to drive over.

(Same morning – delivery room)

I piled everything that I wanted to take with me onto the bed – you can take whatever you like – and followed it down to the delivery suite. I'd picked a dark nightie, on the advice of one of the other girls – stains wouldn't show. Soon we were downstairs in the land of polythene-covered feet and both doctors and nurses in dainty blue headscarves like J cloths! Midwife D. welcomed me and helped me stow all my things in the locker and change into a hospital gown. I'd taken down my rainbow-striped socks with toes, thinking they might be a fun alternative to those long white hospital things, unless everything had to be sterile. They were greeted with delight, however, and everyone who came in was shown my socks; I'm told that while I was pushing later on people were peering in at the door for a view of them!

Then Doctor N. arrived, very charming and kind, to set things up. The stirrups I found comfortable and relaxing. Pelvic floor relaxation and breathing were needed while the doctor had a good grope round inside me – he must have had long fingers, I think! But the news that I was now four centimetres dilated was ample reward. Breaking the waters couldn't be felt at all; all I felt was the warm trickle afterwards as the nurses frantically mopped the floor – someone had forgotten to position the bowl! Nor was there any sensation when the scalp clip was attached to baby's head, very swiftly and expertly. Maybe the baby felt it but I didn't. Then I could sit up again, Midwife D. being a firm believer in the semi-lotus position and the beneficial effects of gravity, thank goodness.

It was odd to see a two-strand flex trailing from one's pussy and plugged into the monitor! Then came the excitement of hearing the baby's heartbeat come over loud and strong, as a light flashed to its rhythm and its pace was shown by a speedometer dial. The glucose and syntocin drip was set up in my left arm, after I'd transferred my watch to the right, and involved no more of a prick than all those blood tests.

56

Everything was plastered on firmly so that I was free to move. A noisy little machine, which one soon got used to, counted the drips and flashed a blue light or an orange alarm light if things went wrong – very sci-fi. The final attachment was a belt round my bulge with a device to monitor the strength of the contractions – a very sophisticated piece of equipment that was fastened together with old-fashioned collar studs! Then that long reel of paper, showing the pattern of the baby's heartbeat and my contractions, started trailing out of the monitor.

The midwife and pupil midwife explained the workings of the bell and intercom and asked about pain-relief. They were quite happy about my wish to rely on my breathing and were very interested in N.C.T. methods. They then disappeared for a coffee.

I was left in peace to write and watch contractions on the monitor. Nurse returned and felt them and confirmed that they were going well; curious, I think, that I didn't regard them as painful. The only snag about successful breathing was that they looked at me and didn't believe what the monitor showed and kept checking contractions with a hand on my tummy – and Nurse T. had hands like ice!

10.00, and just as I wondered where G. was I caught sight of the roof rack turning in the car park. The nurse confirmed, after I'd described the rust patches, that it was Vicky. A hilarious few minutes followed while we watched G. dashing round taking photos of the building, and waved, to be in the shot, even though he couldn't see us. A moment later his arrival was announced over the intercom and the nurse went to meet him. He came in in his blue gown and white hat, laden with all a trained father's equipment – sandwiches, coffee (laced with rum), ice, camera, cassette recorder, and *Winnie-the-Pooh* to read to me if I got bored. (I didn't.) We didn't know that the recorder was on, so had great fun when he played it back. Coffee arrived, and I read the morning's mail that he had brought in while he eagerly took photos of all the machines. Contractions were fairly strong and I usually needed to lean back for support; there was plenty of time to be sociable in between. The hourly bedpan was useful, except that I had a bowel movement each time I used it so was still perched up there for the next contraction – a nuisance.

11.30. Contractions lasting one minute every three minutes. (I never, at any stage, had to breathe down, but could relax once the peak had been passed.) The nurses were having trouble with a wobbly wheel on the drip stand. G. put this right confirming the usefulness of having husbands around, although the nurse joked that it would probably cause an industrial dispute! *Grigor takes over*: M. sick and I was first with the bowl.

12.23. M. first used song (M. – song got boring so I used poetry as well, Keats in particular was very soothing! I went back to the song when things got tough and the conditioned reflex was really needed. Sometimes I slowed down the song to maintain control and sometimes sang aloud; also used pant, pant, blow later on for variety because I liked it.)

12.30. Contractions getting stronger and more even with a sharp increase and gradual decline. The graph did not return to baseline every time.

12.44. M. thought she could feel a pushing sensation but wasn't sure.

12.47. I suggested M. should try a contraction without the breathing but she said the breathing was automatic (M. – or was I chicken?) Just had a long contraction of three minutes. M. doesn't feel like writing and anyway doesn't have time.

1.27. Midwives B. and H. came on duty and were introduced. Syntocin increased.

1.37. Midwife D. decided to examine and there was much cleaning; gloves and masks on. Midwife (pupil) T. also examined with M.'s go-ahead and Midwife D. gave her a fascinating lesson. The dreaded words R.O.P. were spoken! All manipulations were stopped during contractions. Five centimetres dilated.

2.49. Drip changed. Contractions stronger but more separated. M. still feeling fine. (M. – screams from the next room didn't help concentration but soon stopped.)

2.52. M. getting little break between contractions.

3.05. Strong contractions with backache. M. tried to lean on fists and detached drip – blood all over the place but no harm done. M. singing aloud on last contraction – nurses startled and then amused.

3.15. Massage of both thighs helped. M. happier if tummy wasn't touched.

3.20. Very strong contractions. Massage of base of spine with M. sitting up helped.

3.25. M. getting impatient to know how she was dilating.

3.35. M. doing pant, pant, blow.

3.49. M. beginning to feel that she's starting to rip apart. Sister felt head through perincum – still R.O.P.

4.05. Started pushing.

Meg writing: (G. too busy supporting my shoulders to continue record.)

So, no transition stage that I was aware of! The midwife examined as soon as I began to recognise a change in the nature of the contractions and could feel no cervix. What beautiful news. Everyone got into position, G. supporting my shoulders, a nurse supporting each leg. I had no strong urge to push but I did, hard. I couldn't feel much but there was no pain either; it was just hard, satisfying work. Baby's heartbeat slowed but soon steadied. Relaxing between pushes was marvellous, and everyone was encouraging me like mad, telling me when the hair was visible. It was slightly irritating to have the midwife saying 'push to your rectum' and G. translating ('push banana shaped') but they meant the same thing and I was too busy to be bothered by it. After an hour, however, the encouragement began to ring a bit false and I knew we weren't getting far anyway. The doctor looked in and said we could have ten minutes more, then he would have to help. I said, 'Right, baby, we've got a time limit,' and pushed even harder. The sponge came in useful now when there wasn't time to drink from the glass.

They allowed us about twenty-five minutes, the midwives all trying to beat the doctor to it. I think they were more disappointed than we were that it wouldn't be completely 'natural' throughout. The doctor told us that she was stuck and that he would have to turn her with forceps; thank goodness for Michael's demonstration with the doll and the pelvis – we understood fully what had happened and what needed to be done. He said that a local anaesthetic would not be enough, but that he wanted me conscious – and no doubt understood that I didn't want to miss a thing! He began to explain that he wanted quick results and would have a spinal anaesthetic done, but warned me that I would have to lie flat for twenty-four hours. I was horrified – how I pushed on the next contraction! G. went out to change his gear – no question of his being sent out for the delivery – and he heard the anaesthetist saying to the doctor, 'But I can do an epidural.' I was saved! I could cope with the extra few minutes it took to act. The anaesthetist asked G. to wait outside, the first time that this had happened, and he went as the poor chap seemed nervous. I asked for a low dose but he said he would use a drug that would wear off quickly anyway (which it did, in about half an hour, I think). Again, thanks to training I knew what to do right away and curled up on my left side as far as my bulge would allow. It was lovely to lie there and rest after all the pushing. I felt nothing but the tiny prick of the local. It was done very quickly as there was no need to put in a catheter, a single shot only being enough.

Then, for the first time, I really felt the urge to push. I think she turned then as I lay on my side. They let me, but sensation faded before we could get anywhere. G. reappeared in his new outfit, just like the doctor apart from the white wellies. I had to lie flat now, and my peripheral vision was a bit double, but I managed a photo of G., raising my head as far as I could to clear my bulge!

Then off we went to the theatre (which was freezing). I was getting tingly now (with odd thoughts of Socrates and hemlock as the numbness crept up!); then it was into stirrups again for the final gallop.

Grigor writes: I hope that the epidural injection the anaesthetist gave her twenty minutes ago will work; she says her legs and bottom are becoming numb. It had better work – this chap is about to get going with the scissors any moment. I'll concentrate on the camera . . . flash or available light . . . what is it? F4 at fifteen seconds . . . might just manage it if I'm steady. Hey, steady on mate, do you need to cut her that much? I almost felt that myself! It will come out loud and clear on the tape, that's for certain. Click! What a fabulous photo that will make, all that red surrounded by the green drapes!

Meg goes on: The doctor examined – thoroughly; I felt glad of the epidural – and discovered that the cussed little thing had moved and didn't need turning at all. As he said afterwards, it was as well that he checked – embarrassing if he had turned her back the wrong way! We'd been allowed to bring in the camera and tape recorder and the doctor asked G. if he wanted a picture of the birth. Silly question! G. moved into position (thank goodness he wasn't stuck supporting my shoulders) and off we went, pushing (after an hour and a half of practice you can do it, epidural or not), panting, pushing.

Grigor takes over the account: In go the forceps, click, nice and gentle, down, curve upwards, lift and out. What could be simpler?

Meg writes: Then (5.51) the incredible feeling of the bulge I was resting my hands on disappearing. I panted again from sheer surprise! And there she was; a slippery, mauve pair of legs and bottom were lifted into my line of vision.

Grigor: More photos in quick succession then – that first drawn breath, the limp wetness, the wrinkled old face in one so very young – and that glorious, all embracing, body shaking and earth shattering first cry of one's own baby . . .

God, who could possibly miss that moment? It's a girl – it's a girl – it's a girl . . . how absolutely delightful! how marvellous! she's perfect! Thank you – thank you doctor, thank you nurse – thank you everybody, you've been great. How can I thank people enough for such an emotion-saturated experience? Mother and daughter doing well; what a beautiful picture! What a beautiful sight! Mother smiling at the naked, bloody wetness of a first-born. All that pushing, all that anticipation, planning and learning and now here it is, snuggling in, content. Unbelievable!

And Meg writes: She was given to me, there and then, to hold and stroke. 'A modified Leboyer!' said the doctor. She was examined and wrapped up, and G. and I cuddled her while the doctor finished his stitching – and an excellent job he made of it. (*I* couldn't sew holding the needle with long tweezers.)

Then, thanks all round and back we went to the delivery room to share a bottle of wine with the nurses – and no one turned a hair at my drinking too – and try Bridget at the breast which she managed well. Everyone seemed to have plenty of time to help. Then came a luxurious wash and brush up, and another bedpan as they don't like you to wander around right after an epidural, and a long wait for a porter. Then our little procession made its way up to level 4 and B. made her first public appearance in a ward full of people as it was visiting time.

I'd asked for supper but wasn't as hungry as I thought, but what I didn't eat G. did, in spite of his sandwiches during the day. Then came the wonderful but exhausting business of phoning grandparents with a fretful baby who was only too eager to say her piece as well! After that a feed was pretty useless, B. and I both being too tired. Then G. went off, very sleepy, to get a Chinese take-away and drop in on the drama club party to break the news. I settled down to sleep, feeling that nothing on earth could keep me awake. Excitement and my bottom could, however – I still felt as though I had that proverbial grapefruit in my rectum! – so I resorted to Panadol and a sleeping tablet. I woke at 3.30, ravenous, and had a little feast of bananas and biscuits. B. had been hungry too; water and cuddling had not contented her for long and I was woken to feed her at 5.30. Then we both slept well as we deserved after such an exciting and eventful day.

The whole pregnancy and birth was a wonderful experience for us both. We have a tape and a magnificent set of slides and, best of all, the end product – beautiful, ginger-haired Bridget.

THE NEXT TIME ROUND

If a first birth was long and difficult it does not mean that the next one is going to be like that too. Meg's second labour was very different!

We had got things organised the previous night, just in case, and taken some final photos of pregnant me. We didn't dare hope it was the real thing but, after all, contractions were coming regularly at five-minutes intervals. However, they were only mini ones, short and the sensation low down in the back. Or was that significant? After all, my heartburn had suddenly disappeared; could the head have engaged – as it often doesn't do in a multip, until the onset of labour? We were excited but made ourselves go to bed, having chatted and timed contractions for a while over yet another cuppa.

We went to sleep, very well fortunately, as it was only to be for three hours. At 3.30 I was woken by a warm gush that could only be the waters breaking. I'd suspected a slight leak before, having felt small trickles although there was less of the usual sticky discharge. We made another cuppa and decided to wait for a few contractions. Just after 4.00 they started again, still low down in the back and at five-minute intervals. By that time I was having a show as well and needed a pad to cope. We opened the curtains and watched it get light, hearing the dawn chorus with enthusiasm for once! The moon was still in the sky as the sun came up. We got ourselves up in a leisurely way, had some cornflakes and packed, then waited around for a more civilised time to wake Bridget and her godmother. It was lovely standing outside and breathing the fresh morning air through contractions. We saw two magpies in the field. Then a flock of doves flew across the sky from the right – good omens. We went in, woke Bridget, who was delighted that her holiday with Rose was here at last, packed her things and loaded the car. I was feeling a bit sick and belched with contractions – could I be nearing transition? No, silly; still, best to be going. I was beginning to feel the need to get everything organised so we could concentrate on the labour.

We drove into the town through the mist and our friendly neighbourhood black cat paid us the compliment of crossing our path before we set off. Rose answered the door sleepily but quickly and did a marvellous double-take when she realised why we had come! Grigor made a very cool phone-call to the hospital – 'fairly advanced labour' – they were obviously sceptical at the other end! 'Okay, see you in about twenty minutes', and he rang off. We said goodbye to Bridget; in all the checking of lists and packing we hadn't got round to mentioning that baby was on its way, but now we were certain and told her. Her face lit up, and she waved goodbye with great excitement. We set off on a swift, lovely drive on early morning deserted roads.

Contractions by now were a bit uncomfortable and I still felt slightly sick. There was pressure on the sacrum and pubic arch, similar to the 'splitting open' feeling I remembered from late first stage last time. One or two of the corners had to be taken very slowly, Grigor driving with one eye on me and one on the road! We arrived at the hospital – plenty of space in the car park for once! – and walked up to the doors, pausing to lean on the railings for a contraction. We were shown into a prep. room, footsteps approached down the corridor, and Grigor popped his head out to exclaim, 'Fantastic! What a coincidence – Sister D.' The very midwife who had been with us for much of the time last time! Lots of chat followed; so exciting it was that I went to the loo with my little paper cup for a specimen and clean forgot until I'd finished, then knocked it over. She finally had a miserable teaspoonful to test!

At the second attempt we found a nightie with tapes on

the back and Sister D. checked a contraction and baby's heartbeat. I began to think my suspicions that we might be quite well on were correct when the midwife said 'But this is fantastic, quite amazing.' She laughed when I enjoyed being swabbed down with cold antiseptic and said that that confirmed that I was really in labour. She began to examine me internally, then paused for a contraction, watching me. That one felt different part way through and she said afterwards that she could see from the change of expression in my eyes that I was in transition. There's experience for you. The examination confirmed that I was at least eight centimetres dilated and the next couple of contractions would take up the anterior lip. 'You'll have the baby within half an hour. Porter!' Sister D. announced with great delight that she would deliver us herself. 'All the students are down in observation and they've done all their births; I'm going to be selfish.' We were thrilled too.

The porter arrived and took us to 'one of the window rooms' and we sped along the sunlit corridor. I'd wondered if the feeling in my throat on the previous contraction was the beginning of the pushing urge and the next one confirmed it, so it was 'pant, pant, blow' all the way to the delivery room. The delivery bed felt lovely and firm and business-like, and the view outside was magnificent. There was little time to luxuriate, however, or even to get properly into position; the pushing urge was overwhelming. I made a real mess of the first contraction, then collected myself and started working hard. Grigor was taking photos from every angle and Sister D. was scrubbing up. Between contractions we chatted.

Then there was the incredible sensation of the head hard between the pelvic bones and Sister D. asked if the perineum felt very stretched. It didn't to me and we let things go for another contraction but it did seem to be holding things back so we agreed to an episiotomy. The local anaesthetic was injected and I knew that on the next push the cut would be made; I felt a bit inhibited about that one! Willpower won, however, there was the sound of the cut, then 'pant, pant!' Grigor said later that the midwife was juggling madly to put aside the scissors and take the head. I panted and whimpered and groaned with excitement. The head was born and I felt it turn, then had to push again for the shoulders. Where I got the strength for that push from I don't know! Grigor yelled 'David!' and somewhere amid all the excitement I asked for the cord to be left uncut for a few minutes. The next instant I was taking him, all pink and making little noises, and stroking a back still thick with vernix. We cuddled and crooned and he fell asleep, while the cord went on pulsing for some time. It felt slippery and amazingly strong and firm. At last it stopped and Sister D. asked if she could cut it. Meanwhile a belated shot of syntometrine had been given and with a little cord traction and a push from me (hard to push on something soft) the placenta was born. We had a good look at it, the baby's side lined with a smooth membrane very different from the rough sheet I was holding over him now. Sister D. checked him briefly and Grigor cuddled him while I was tidied up a bit and arranged myself to await a doctor do to the stitching. We celebrated with wine. David was taken to be cleaned up, which he apparently hated, and Grigor and I sat at peace.

At last the doctor arrived, thirty-two weeks pregnant and having trouble in getting a gown to meet at the back! Stitching wasn't comfortable for her either – the position gave her back-ache. I reminded them that the local for the episiotomy had been put in some time before, and plenty more was added. Even so, one or two stitches weren't covered. Relaxing toward the stitching and breathing helped, however, although I was occasionally caught unawares as baby was back and the conversation good. I couldn't pant and talk! Even so, it seemed to take a long time, then the doctor was off, with our good wishes for her own baby.

A much needed wash-down for me followed. A bed pan was also very welcome. Grigor ate his sandwiches and we shared some chocolate, marvellous as we were starving and

I'd missed breakfast upstairs. Then another cup of tea arrived and I fed David during the usual long wait for bed and porter. He caught on to the idea very well, and I suppose that this time I was more experienced. It was certainly good to be feeding again. The tall young porter with the beautiful face who had wheeled us down wheeled us back, then we had to wait again for another porter to take us upstairs. For that morning we had a room to ourselves and all three of us dozed, and chatted, very pleased with outselves, until it was time to phone our parents and tell the rest of the world about our new and beautiful son.

Grigor's account of the second labour: There I was, innocently hoovering the bedroom floor . . . Suddenly there SHE was – all 36–48–36 of her – looking most appetising . . . a passionate glint in her eye, her long hair streaming over proud, blue-veined cherry breasts, and a bathed, clean, shaved pussy – moist, open, inviting . . .

It hadn't taken long and I found that the hoover was still running, also becoming very hot; its run-down whine reflected exactly our post-coital slowing to stop. What time is it? Just 6.30 p.m. well, prostaglandin, get to work and soften up that ripe cervix! Hope my thrusts didn't disturb too much. I didn't feel anything hard – I wonder if the head is engaged in the pelvis! It will be, soon enough.

A cup of tea, then on with the hoovering; no more disturbances this time. But all our noises did disturb our first-born – wondering what Mum is up to, I suppose. I'd better go to reassure her that all is well; once her mother gets going the whole terrace gets to hear of it!

Our first-born, when she arrived, decided to be awkward. That was two years ago now but it seems like yesterday. She got her head stuck on the way out. We had the full treatment to get her born – induction, drip, fetal scalp clip, monitor, and eventually the operating thearte for a forceps delivery.

Thank goodness we had both been to antenatal classes together so that I had some idea of what was happening and

68

why. It was all very exciting – the bright lights, the ritual scrubbing up, gowns, the precise positioning of all those sterile instruments, the gentle, unhurried opening of sealed paper packages . . . all that experience and training waiting, routines to be adhered to precisely, everything needing to be done just right, all that knowledge!

So I wonder what will happen this time . . . She probably won't need any analgesia unless we go to the theatre again. She coped well with her breathing last time – boy, did that midwife jump when we both burst into song at the height of a contraction! It suppose it did seem a bit strange to sing 'It's been a hard day's night' in the middle of the afternoon.

What was that, darling? Not a Braxton Hicks . . . you mean you think it could be a real contraction and not a mock one? No, I don't believe it. It can't have started yet, why, I haven't revised all of Belinda's notes! What's the time, 10.40 p.m.? Don't panic, mate, she's having you on; there's plenty of time. Or is there? They arc all coming at regular intervals and persisting . . . Just don't let yourself get excited . . . Excited!

Change the subject. What's for supper? Snails? Great! I just don't fancy these snails; they are delicious with all that lovely garlic butter, but my stomach is just as excited as it was on our wedding morning!

At least everything is ready, or is it? Have you checked the list? Look, we haven't had a dummy run; what do we need to get? Is there a list for us and one for Ginger sleeping peacefully upstairs? Just don't panic, don't get excited, you've gone through this before. Keep calm, try to tidy up and make her feel you are coolly efficient. Get some more small ice cubes made up, empty the dishwasher without breaking anything, rinse out the thermos, make a cup of tea . . . So they are still coming at five minute intervals, but of short duration and not very strong. I wonder. 12.20 – better get to bed and try to get some sleep. Everything we planned at classes is ready.

What a hell of a time to wake a bloke up! 3.30 a.m. What?

The waters? Never ... that's only a tiny amount, no, maybe not so tiny – thank goodness we put a blanket over the mattress just in case. Are you sure, a slight pinkish stain? Yes, that certainly does look like small streaks of blood on that tissue. Oh. Well, let's move nice and slowly.

Cup of tea? Naturally! How very convenient that you had a bath with daughter this evening! She will be delighted; she has been looking forward to her little holiday with her godmother for weeks. Just as well that dummy run was successful, when she stayed there while we had that fantastic weekend in London on our wedding anniversary. 4.00 a.m. and contractions restart at five-minute intervals, so we take the suitcase downstairs. Things get packed into the hold-all, ice into the thermos; you get your hair brushed and your eyes painted. A nice simple bowl of cornflakes – great, just what we need. I go out to water the tomatoes. What a fabulous sunrise! We stand looking at the grey-green mist over the meadow. For once there are two magpies, and a flock of doves flies noisily over the house from our right – what a picture, what a memory! We have a nice gentle cuddle on the doorstep, breathing in the cold dawn air, knowing confidently and together that this is it. There are dewdrops on the lavender, a cheerful, twittering dawn chorus and a blood red sun rising gently over the farm buildings.

Let's move ... pack the car, check the list. 5.35. We gently wake up daughter who is delighted that at last she is to have her holiday. Her eyes open wide as she says 'Rose'. Change her – do we take her potty? She was doing quite well the previous afternoon with nothing on in the sun. No, let's not bother, plenty of time for that another day. Get her dressed, she'll have breakfast later.

By now Mum is needing to stop whatever she is doing to lean on things and breathe through contractions, which are coming at three-minute intervals. I move quickly and efficiently and the car is loaded.

The car starts; damn, it just won't go into first gear; keep calm, don't sheer off the gear stick; try reverse. It works –

great! Tiggy, our local black neutered tomcat walks calmly in front of us from right to left.

Godmother wasn't expecting us to arrive at six o'clock in the morning! It took her a full minute to register what was happening – then a smile of delight appeared on her kind face. There was a tearful embrace that was broken off by yet another contraction. I phone the hospital and a sceptical sister records that my wife is in a fairly advanced stage of labour. Never mind, she will believe us soon enough. Gentle around the corners and drive like hell on the straight bits. We know the route well, and what luck that it is daylight and a quiet Sunday morning before a bank holiday, hardly anyone around.

My sympathy to fathers who panic, who get lost, who run out of petrol, who have a gasket blow, or a puncture, who crash the car or who have to drive a mountainous groaning, contracting lump through rush hour traffic! We park the car and have to stop to lean on the white fence to get through another contraction. At 6.30 we are in an examination room and – lo and behold – it's Sister D. – the same superb, experienced midwife who was with us last time! We were most lucky and most grateful.

A speedy examination followed. Contractions were coming well, photos were good, breathing was right . . . and an internal reveals that the cervix is eight centimetres dilated already. 'Porter!' To the delivery room, fast; we have about half an hour.

Quickly we load the bed with all our bits and pieces. Mother is obviously delighted and excited that she has got so far without realising it. I quickly get a gown and help to open doors and steer the bed around the corners. She gets onto the delivery bed and at once there is another contraction. Again those mysterious sterile packages appear on the trolley and the bottom half of the bed is removed. We three are together, ready, doing it all. What fun! I wouldn't miss this for all the cup finals that ever were or ever would be!

She needs to push – blow, pant, pant, blow – she didn't

push; what superb self-control, and a tremendous sense of satisfaction – the training works again. The midwife is scrubbed up so I slosh a capful of antiseptic into the bowl, adjust the lamp and switch on the heater. Meg holds the fetal stethoscope steady on her tum while baby's heartbeat is checked. Now, pushing and photos. I can see the head: it looks like ginger hair. Marvellous, we're going fine; there's lots of encouragement and for a moment mother thought she had forgotten how to push. But it's no good; perhaps it was the scar tissue from the old episiotomy that wouldn't stretch but it has to be done again. Ah well, hedgehog bottom, here we go.

Lots more photos; very messy but never mind. The head has turned the corner, lots of it showing now . . . click . . . gently does it as the rubber glove steadies it out . . . click . . . here comes the shoulder . . . click . . . then the back, then out with a slither . . . click . . . easy! Again that first breath and ecstatic cry – when time stops and life has a meaning. The babe, gently raised and placed in its mother's arms, soon stops its noise and snores to sleep. The coiled blue and white cord, still gently pulsating, links the mother to that former part of herself that now snuggles, contented, in her arms. Mother and son are doing well.

JUSTIN BECAME THE FOCAL POINT OF MY VERY EXISTENCE

In the back of this woman's mind during pregnancy was her own mother's suffering in childbirth: 'a bit Dostoevskyish. She nearly died with the first . . . I always felt that childbirth was sweating endurance, pain like no other.'

A friend had come to dinner the night before and Justin had stayed up late to watch the World Cup; besides the baby wasn't due for another nine days.

So when labour started with strong pains (1) at about 3.00 a.m., my sleepy reaction was to ignore the whole thing. It just wasn't convenient. Justin would be tired, my suitcase wasn't fully packed, we had a party to go to that evening, and I didn't want to have the baby on Saturday 13th – which was the following day.

Those thoughts came and receded as I hovered between sleeping and waking. I was dimly aware that I should be awake to be prepared for the next contraction, but the first two or three were widely spaced (by perhaps half an hour), were not too strong and I managed to breathe through them quite satisfactorily.

At about 5 o'clock Justin, half waking to find me vigorously breathing over a contraction, murmured, 'That's very good, darling', apparently thinking I was practising.

'It hurts,' I said, and then asked him to forgive me if I was horrid to him during the contractions. Everything went very fast then. We were both fully awake but I, in the grip of very frequent contractions, was unable to gather my thoughts and to realise how quickly things were moving. I vomited after each contraction, which I must admit I didn't always control too well, although when I did ride one successfully with very light mouth-centred breathing, I had a sense of satisfaction and achievement.

I would like to explain my impression of the contractions at this stage, because I certainly found them much different to what I had expected. I had been used to Braxton-Hicks contractions during late pregnancy, and these gave a definite sensation of the womb drawing itself in, usually painlessly but sometimes with discomfort. In early labour, however, I had no contracting sensation, only a mounting crescendo of pain unlike any other pain I had experiencend. I gave way to it once or twice and writhed in the classic style while clenching the pillows, but Justin was there to hold me and breathe with me.

Then came the moment I think of as the climax of the labour. I ran to the lavatory without knowing why but I did feel an urgent need to get there. Whilst sitting I felt I'd had several more contractions, but it could have been just one long contraction. It culminated in an overwhelming emotional onslaught – not a physical pain, but a sort of mental extremis, even anguish in which even its purpose – that of having a baby – was lost. Then suddenly the waters broke with a great spurt and I was lifted with the most marvellous sense of relief. This was followed by a blissful few minutes before the next contraction. Little did I realise, however, that I was already almost fully dilated and about to go into the second stage of labour.

From then on the drama became tinged with comedy, and I can truly say in retrospect that I actually enjoyed it. It was then that Justin became the focal point of my very existence. I virtually handed myself over to him; my reliance on him was total. I heard him calmly phoning the hospital and then the ambulance while I threw things at random into my suitcase – this between rushing to sit on the side of the bed for another contraction. But it was quite different now. Pain was no longer to the forefront. My body was eagerly and vigorously at work and I started to bear down. 'I'm going to push!

74

I'm going to push!' I grunted inaccurately, pushing hard. 'No!' said Justin, holding me tight, 'Breathe, breathe!' Pant, pant, pant, blow, blow;(2) he forced me to breathe. But we got to the ambulance without too much pushing, and covered the fifteen minute journey in what seemed to me like a flash.

I don't remember getting out of the ambulance, but there we were in the main entrance, with me sitting in a wheelchair and a man insistently demanding a blue card. Miraculously, Justin found it and off we went along corridors. As each further contraction came I would say 'Justin!' and we stopped and breathed and grunted, to the amazement of passers-by, while the chairpusher helpfully repeated Justin's words, 'That's right, dear. You breathe.'

Up in the lift we went and into the labour ward we rushed. I practically leaped on to the bed and heard the midwife say that I was fully dilated and could push now. So away we went. Justin was the only person I saw or noticed. He stood beside me in a white gown and mask and as every contraction started I said 'Justin' and he put his arm under my head and held my leg under the knee. Voices told me to push as hard and as long as I could, down into the rectum. And I pushed, eyes tightly shut, going purple in the face I'm sure, with every ounce of my strength. But being held in that position, head forward and knees up, was a wonderful help. I think I would have found it terribly difficult without this brace. The rest between each effort seemed blissfully long, and I lay completely relaxed and without anxiety. Then we'd start again and I could hear Justin, his face close to mine, pushing involuntarily as I did, while somewhere voices encouraged and the baby's head pushed down like a big, hard ball. 'It's going to come out of the wrong hole,' I muttered.

On we went, Justin and I, and it was like running a marathon. At one point I noticed Justin was sitting on a stool instead of standing beside me and saw a nurse hand him another mask. I didn't know then that we had been running our marathon here for a full hour. I was aware of feeling increasingly tired. The muscles in my legs trembled with fatigue and sweat rolled off me. Yet I was mentally relaxed and when I heard the doctor, who had arrived at some time during the proceedings, saying calmly that he would help the baby out with forceps, I still felt no anxiety.

My feet were put into stirrups and I was given two little jabs of local anaesthetic. I could still push, he said, so I pushed again. The head came through, then the body with a satisfactorily slither, and I saw the baby's feet as Justin said 'It's a boy.'

He was put into my arms, looking a regular tough guy and with one eye closed as if he'd been in a fight.(3) His little body felt deliciously fat. Then Justin and I were left alone and I knew that we had been through an experience together with was beyond compare – exhilarating and marvellous. I also know that without him and our combined knowledge, I could never have run the course as I did. And I have been happier than I can say ever since, and so grateful.

Justin's version:

THERE WAS ONLY ONE PERSON IN THE WHOLE WORLD – CLARE

Mr Z. had grown-up children by his first marriage and had never had anything to do with the birth of his other children. It took quite a lot of courage for an older and sophisticated man to start out on a new experience of this kind, and to learn how to support his wife in a task which conventionally has been a matter for women only.

I woke to hear Clare doing rapid, upper breathing and, thinking she was practising with a light contraction, mumbled, 'That's very good, darling, very good.' But the breathing continued and there was no immediate reply.

Still half submerged I struggled to the surface with the dawning realisation that this was going to be the day the baby would be born. 'God, no. Not after a late night and a little too much whisky. Not today.' It was 5.00 a.m. and already light. I cursed myself for a fool and wished I had gone to bed early. Clare then told me her contractions were severe, so I rose, got out the books for a quick refresher course, fetched a large pocket watch to check the frequencies of contractions, and put the kettle on for a cup of coffee. As a mixture of excitement and anxiety rose in me, the cobwebs began to break away and, as I waited for the next contraction, I tried to remain calm. It came within five minutes and I encouraged her to do the proper breathing. The next took ten minutes to arrive. Immediately after it was over, Clare went to the loo and in a moment called to say that the waters had broken. I began hurriedly to get dressed, got her back on to the bed, rang the hospital, to tell them what had happened, then rang for an ambulance. With the next contraction Clare started to push while I did all I could to encourage her not to, holding her and breathing with her close to her face. It was not long before the ambulance arrived, but we had to wait until another contraction was over before she could make her way down to it. Somehow an hour had passed since I first woke.

In the ambulance I began to give her spinal massage and accidentally felt the large lump at the bottom of her spine which was the baby's head trying to emerge. I knew then that she was pretty well fully dilated, and knew also that I would have to work hard to try and stop her pushing, if the baby was not to be born on the way. With each effort, things around me became more irrelevant and remote, so great was my concentration on Clare alone. When we reached the hospital we got her into a wheelchair when somebody asked for the 'Blue Card'. Jesus, a blue card! What the hell's a blue card got to do with it? It apparently had a lot to do with it. 'If you haven't got a blue card,' went on the tired voice of a minor bureaucrat in a dust coat, 'you might be here for hours.' Thankfully, Clare said it was in her handbag. Her handbag was in her suitcase and I dived for it anxiously. Women's handbags have always been a kind of mysterious lucky-dip to me, but somehow the magic card, as if wishing to help, poked a corner up in the scramble and we set off along the corridor.

Three times in the labyrinths of the hospital we stopped on Clare's request. Three times I found myself down on my knees in front of her, alternately panting rapidly near her face and shouting at her to stop pushing, wishing desperately at least to reach the sanctity of the more hygenic labour ward, rather than be seated on the ground with a new baby in my arms amidst passing feet. When we got there everything happened quickly. As I whipped off my jacket, somebody was immediately tying me into a gown and handing me a mask as Clare was put on the labour bed. The midwife asked her if she wanted gas and she said yes. I said no and put the gas mask away. Clare accepted this overruling quite readily and we began to work. With each contraction I hooked her left leg over my arm and supported the back of her head in my right, going grunt for grunt with her although not realising it at the time. My emotions were becoming stronger with each contraction, a mixture of excitement and anxiety. It is difficult to explain the power of these feelings, and it is perhaps best described with an analogy – much as I distrust analogies. But it was like having a grip on somebody you loved who had just fallen over a cliff; fighting to hang on to them with total, unconscious disregard for your own safety, not sure how you were going to make it to save them, but determined, above all else, to do so and at the same time having to assure them that everything was perfectly all right. There was only one person in the whole world at this time and that was Clare. The others were vague characters from a dream – onlookers, advisers, people with safety equipment which could not yet be used.

I felt that I was the only one in physical contact, the only one with a grip, and that it all depended on me and on me alone. Despite this, however, there was a moment when I thought I might faint with the effort and quickly turned to a sink behind me for a drink of water, forcing myself not to give way. As this was between contractions when I was trying to get Clare to relax, I was also a little ashamed, for at the same time Clare was asked to sign an 'Operation if Necessary' form, and did so with apparent ease.

We went on working together like this and with each effort I could see a little bit more of the baby's head until a section about three inches in diameter was showing. It was very dark-looking with waved hair. At one stage someone removed from me what was by now a sodden mask and it was not until then I realised how much I was sweating – a combination of effort, emotion, and the hot morning. Handed a fresh mask, I put it on and we continued. My anxiety at this stage began to fade a little, mostly perhaps because Clare seemed to me more at ease, relaxing well between pushes and taking it magnificently. But the other emotions were just as strong. I looked at the clock to see what time was passing, so knew that we had been working together for just over an hour, although it could have been minutes had I used my own sense of time. It was then that the doctor, who had already examined her, told me that it was a big baby, that he was going to cut and help it out. He asked me if I was going to leave, but to have deserted Clare then would have been impossible for me. I answered rather aggressively that I was staying there, and remained by her side. He didn't argue but got down to work. Clare's legs were slung up, the bottom half of the bed lowered, preparation for a local anaesthetic made, a couple of jabs given, then the light surgery. It was all very neat, efficient and swift. He then said to us, 'All right, you still do most of the work.' On the following contraction Clare pushed steadily down while the doctor, with the forceps in, pulled forcefully but gently out. The head came out and the doctor, turning it, eased out the rest until it lay born in the midwife's hands. A boy. The time was only 8.10 a.m.

The baby was bluish in colour at first and only slightly bruised, but perfect in every other respect that one could see.

79

It was soon followed by the placenta which the doctor examined thoroughly. Meanwhile the cord was being cut, after which the baby was taken across the ward to have the fluids sucked out. But there was still a very strong tension in me as I looked from Clare to the baby, waiting for what seemed an interminable time, but which was probably a matter of seconds. Then it cried. It was a moment of supreme relief and joy to see Clare's face. What stopped me from crying myself I don't know – probably my dour Scottish blood – but I cannot remember feeling so utterly full of anything in my life.

From then on it was almost routine. The doctor quickly stitched Clare as we spoke quietly to each other. The baby was put in her arms for a short while before being taken away. Then it seemed everybody was out of the place and a nurse came in with a tea tray. So we had a cup of tea together and that was the way it was.

Oh no, not quite: I must not forget this. The following morning I awoke with muscular pains in my stomach and that was the way it was, too. After all, *WE'd* just had an 8 lb 2 oz baby.

Notes

1. Note that women use words in very different ways. Here were 'strong pains', and yet this mother was 'hovering between sleeping and waking'.
2. This quick breathing interspersed with blowing out allows the cervix to open fully without the baby being pressed down into it too early.
3. Sometimes after a forceps delivery pressure on a facial nerve causes temporary paralysis of one side of the baby's face. This only lasts a few days, but can mean that he looks as if he had been in a punch-up.

THE INCREDIBLE JOY THAT WELLS UP WITH THAT FIRST CRY

I had a most relaxed and happy pregnancy up to the last fortnight. Then everything seemed to happen to get me down, culminating a week beforehand in the news that my only brother, a naval officer of 24, we all adored, had been killed. After being knocked sideways for a bit I realised that I had to make a decision to get right on top of the situation, for my sake and the baby's; otherwise I would go right down and start off its life on a very depressed note. After a few days I refused to look back and tried to be thoroughly grateful for all the wonderful times we had had. I then felt very much closer to him, and a very happy frame of mind returned.

Things started to happen on Saturday. I felt some twinges at lunchtime and thought this was probably it. My husband was delighted (he had been impatient for weeks), as he was starting at the Head Office in London on Monday and wanted to be around (note change of heart!). To consolidate matters we took the dog for a run on the downs at twilight. It was a wonderful occasion. We have never felt closer or more in love. By the time we got home I found contractions coming every ten minutes. I later had a lovely, relaxing, luxurious bath – and everything promptly stopped! Anyway, by midnight they were back again at five-minute intervals, so we decided to go. I had been doing slow breathing all the while and enjoyed each contraction. We both found it so exciting.

At the hospital I was shaved and given an enema. The nurse then left me to 'sleep'. Ha Ha! They were still about five minutes apart, but far too strong to make sleep possible. These contractions went on at the same interval but with increasing intensity through the night. I managed with my breathing happily, though I found deep breathing at the start impossible, but the shallow mouth-centred for the height a great help.

When the Matron came on at 10.30 a.m. the contractions were getting hefty. She came and put her arm round me and said 'I think you've had enough. I do appreciate what you are doing, but you are my responsibility and I'm going to make things easier for you and hurry things up.' I tried to tell her that I was coping – but she obviously felt I was in more pain than I was. I had some pethidine and some pills to speed matters. The pethidine made me sleep between contractions, but I could still control my breathing during them.

At about 1 o'clock contractions became almost continuous and extremely strong. By 2.00 p.m. I suddenly wanted to push – and changed to mouth-centred and a blow and staved it off till Sister came. I then had to be hurried to the delivery room on foot. After about four pushes in which I felt the head come round, I asked when to pant and was told to do so next time. Then with one slight push the baby came.

I know the next moments have been so well described hundreds of times before me, but the incredible joy that first cry wells up in one is so momentous as to defy description. It is too spiritual for even a poet's words. She gave three little bleats, that was all. The rest of her slid through, and the Sister told me she was a girl and I didn't know whether to laugh or cry. They lifted her up for me to see, after clamping the cord, and she was perfect. Her large, bright eyes gave me a searching look, as if to say, 'So that's what you look like.' The freedom, lightness, energy and joy I felt then has stayed with me since. She was 7 lb 6 oz. After the birth, at 2.15 p.m. I felt incredibly well and awake, and could have done the Highland Fling then and there. I'm sure this wouldn't have been so without having been fairly successful with natural childbirth methods. In fact there was another girl in the next room who was running parallel with me and she followed an identical course. I gather she took about three days to recover from her experience and the depression and tiredness that followed.

Every day my love for my darling little girl grows stronger, if that is possible, since I adored her the moment I saw her. I love feeding her – not in an erotic sense, but more, to use that horrible woman's magazine word, the togetherness – the closeness. I feel it is my love that is passing between us. The most marvellous time is in the early morning when one has forgotten one has a baby; to be awoken with the sight of that little bundle is such a thrill!

The kindness and cheerfulness I have met in the hospital have been wonderful, and I have had a complete rest. The Matron's criterion is love and compassion and she manages to combine it with efficiency and to make a very happy, intimate atmosphere.

I really do appreciate the great help the classes were to me, and of course they were great fun as well. I certainly look back at birth with pleasure, and hope to have several more babies.

LABOUR BETWEEN LUNCH AND TEA

I woke at 1.00 a.m. with some cramp in my legs followed by a couple of twinges and a feeling of great heaviness. There were no further indications of labour, so later I had a bath and went to bed, to waken a couple of hours later with more twinges, rather like pre-menstrual pains.

Between 2.00 and 3.00 p.m., I had lunch – sausage rolls, Chelsea bun, tea, with an accompaniment of very mild contractions of about a quarter of a minute in length and about ten minutes to a quarter of an hour apart. I tried middle chest breathing for these, but my mother-in-law looked so concerned that I decided not to bother any more.

At about 3 o'clock I went upstairs and sat on a bed reading, feeling sleepy between contractions, and breathing for them with shallow chest breathing, as they were now stronger. I found that I preferred to lean, standing up, with my hands resting on a low divan, with my feet apart about a yard or so from the divan. I decided that labour had definitely started, even though the contractions were mild and flat, so at 3.30 p.m. rang my husband and asked him to come home from work, and went back to the bedroom. My mother-in-law said she'd make a cup of tea for me, so I came down to get it and had another contraction half-way upstairs as my husband came in. He rang the hospital and the doctor as I was having the next contraction, and the waters broke with a ping and a splash on to the bedroom floor, and what a shock! – I could feel the baby's head pressing *right* down, my body wide open, and there was the second stage! I called to Bob and told him there wasn't time to get to the hospital, I'd have the baby in the bathroom, it was so difficult to walk! I was so silly. All I wanted to do was wash my briefs, as the mucus plug and show had come away and I didn't want to leave them for in-laws to find. The other thing was for Bob to scrub the carpet where the waters had shot out. We did all this before the next contraction.

After the next contraction we went downstairs. Another contraction by the front door. Up to the car, and I couldn't think how I could actually step into it – and my dressing gown was still on, in the pouring rain. Another contraction – into the car. And we swerved up to the hospital only about five minutes away at about 3.50 p.m. Bob dashed in to find a nurse, and Sister appeared at the door. She just beckoned and said, 'Come ON!'

I must say I couldn't help wondering whether I was imagining it, as these were very mild contractions too, with no sudden point of almost uncontrollable pushing. They were like first stage contractions in shape, and the breathing was like this: puff, puff, puff, blow-blow-blow-*blow* . . . *blow* . . . *BLOW* – very slow and steady blowing out. And that would be the end of the contraction.

My doctor didn't arrive until after the baby was born. They hustled me into a chair and trundled it along the corridor to the delivery room. I started to get undressed. I leaned on the delivery table, blowing out. The Sister shaved me. The labour was still fantastically mild.

I asked if I could push – or rather explained why I was blowing out, and she said – 'Oh, any time you like, push'. I said I didn't want to push against an insufficiently dilated cervix, and went on blowing out. She asked had my husband been to classes, and nodded to the other nurse to bring him in. She said – 'Your baby's just sitting here, waiting to be born.' Bob came in and could see the baby's hair, and pushing started.

He supported my back and shoulders, rounded, for pushing. Sister said did I want to lie on my side, and I said not unless it was easier for her. She said it wasn't. There was still no sweeping urge to push. It was just slow and steady. The baby was born at 4.30 p.m., a girl weighing 8 lb 9½ oz. There was a very small tear, which the Sister stitched. She said they called it a buttonhole.

By 6 o'clock I was sitting up in bed having sausages again, this time sausage and mash!

The baby fed very well, and the milk supply was so good that she never lost her birth weight, and had gained 3 oz, when I came home on the sixth day. They said it was very unusual for a breastfed baby. I can't praise them enough for their attitude over breastfeeding. We were allowed as much time as we wanted, the nurses only coming in after half to three-quarters of an hour to ask if we had finished. It didn't seem to occur to them that we (or *I*, and I was the only one breastfeeding – sadly – in such surroundings) would need a bottle.

This labour was fantastically easy, almost not a labour at all – in fact, a bit disappointing, as I would have liked to be 'tossed and lost' a little bit, and to be able to control it with breathing of course.

Many thanks for the insight we gained, and helping us to attain this confidence and composure during labour.

LIKE A WINKLE ON A ROCK

*Not all women, however well prepared, enjoy childbirth —
and certainly a great many feel no special ecstasy. It is important to allow a woman her own feelings, and not to deny
them their validity in any way by stimulating emotions. This
mother found nothing 'spiritual' or 'revealing' in her labour,
but felt it a job well done.*

The general impression was that the methods of relaxation
worked. I should have felt completely at sea without the
knowledge, even though we had a most helpful and sympathetic midwife, and I had Julian's hand to hang on to. You
will gather from this that I did not find it an uplifting experience, but I did get a lot of satisfaction from being able to
control myself. I'm sure it was a very good thing for Serena.
She is marvellous!

Last four weeks of pregnancy; the baby's head was in mid-
cavity, but as the pelvis was large, it was able to swivel
around freely.
Week preceding: the baby was ROA, (1) but with first few
contractions it changed to LOA. (2)
1.30 p.m. Contractions started, and at this stage fairly long
slow breaths were helpful.
About 5.00 p.m. The contractions got fiercer, and shallower
breathing with a few odd long breaths seemed to work.
About 6.30 p.m. As it got to four fingers and the transition,
fast light breathing worked best. All this time I was on
my side, but when we thought the second stage was getting near, I turned on my back to push the baby free. At

four fingers I had a small injection of pethidine, and was very glad of it, as things turned out.

About 8 p.m. The baby was kicking heftily most of the time and at four fingers the midwife believes the head moved to ROP.(3) This and the fact that it was not well flexed explain the great difficulty and discomfort which ensued with the anterior lip. We all struggled for hours to loose it. I turned back to my side position eventually.

Midnight. After a fifteen-minute pause during which the contractions stopped altogether (a welcome and luxurious rest to me), suddenly I was able to push.

12.15 a.m. The first two contractions I didn't make much use of, but then got the hang of bearing down while releasing the pelvic floor. The baby was born at 1.45 a.m.

Her insufficiently flexed head was a strain on the perineum and made the delivery awkward for the nurse; nevertheless, the perineum had only a first degree tear.

The doctor arrived at an awkward stage in the transition, when we were trying treating a contraction as first stage-type instead of looking for pushes. The shallow rapid breathing worked beautifully.

Doctor: Was *that* a contraction?

Midwife: Yes, a *good* one.

Doctor: Well, I'll read the Sunday paper in the next room until something more interesting (dramatic?) happens.

My husband reminded me of all the things I was forgetting, stuffed wet sponges in my mouth, gave me powerful mixes of PLJ and glucose (most refreshing) and startling accounts of first sight of the baby's hair. ('It looks the colour of a winkle – after all it *is* a marine animal still!') It must be a great deprivation not to have your husband with you.

Notes

1. Right occipito-anterior i.e. on the mother's right side, facing the back.

2. Left occipito-anterior i.e. on the mother's left side, facing the back.
3. Right occipito-posterior, i.e. on the mother's right side, facing to the front, a less favourable position.

THE FIRST SUNNY DAY IN SPRING

Some women seem to do their best when they have an atten-
tive and admiring audience! This is a case in point. She was
probably helped a great deal by having visitors, and certainly
avoided going into hospital too soon – a common mistake
when the first baby is on the way.

Cressida, my baby daughter, was three weeks late, weighing
8 lb 5 oz.

I had only been having noticeable Braxton-Hicks contractions for a week, so did not think anything of the mild but
fairly regular ones, that started when I was having a cup of
tea reading the *Observer* on Sunday. I was going into hospital
the next day to have the baby induced, so had quite given up
hope of anything happening of its own accord. Fairly soon it
was apparent that these contractions were really quite regular
– one every 40–45 minutes, although they were not in the
slightest bit painful, just efficient muscle-working in my back
and tummy – very pleasant in fact. After three of them I told
Charles, who was sawing logs. He looked mildly pleased and
carried on with what he was doing. He had also given up
hope of the baby arriving until I went into hospital. We had
invited my sister and her boyfriend and another couple for
the day, and they arrived at about 11.30.

I felt elated and slightly drunk for no apparent reason and
the contractions assumed a definite pattern. One after 20
minutes, one after 40, one after 20, etc. My sister took me for
a drive while the men went to the pub for a drink. It was a
wonderful day, very hot and sunny, and I couldn't bear the
thought of missing it all staying inside. When we got back
and I started cooking the lunch the contractions got quite

strong. I was perfectly comfortable though, and leant against the cooker and let my tummy hang, doing the deep breathing, and as they only came every 20 minutes it didn't disturb the roast lamb too much, and lunch was on time. Everyone was trying so hard to pretend nothing was happening and that they were entertained frequently by a woman in labour, but eventually they gave up and goggled with unfeigned fascination when I started shallow chest breathing when the contractions were quite strong, coming every ten minutes. I was by this time sitting in an armchair in a corner. I still felt terribly happy and elated and kept saying what a lovely day it was to be having a baby.

I was still loath to ring up the hospital. I knew that Charles would come with me, but it was a lovely day, the park was looking beautiful and I was surrounded by our best friends. I was completely happy and wanted it to go on as long as possible. My sister, although quite young and unmarried, was absolutely marvellous. She did all the washing up and tidying and packed my bag for me – terribly calm all the time. The other girl was obviously expecting me to produce a towel and start biting on it every minute, she had not had any children, but had three sisters, all of whom are inclined to go on a bit about the horrors of childbirth, and was amazed at my 'fortitude and endurance'.

At 4 o'clock the waters broke (everyone sitting around having tea). I hobbled into the bathroom and decided that I had really better get a move on, as after that contractions came every three minutes and were very strong. I was bundled into the car and we rushed off, after ringing the hospital, and of course got stuck in a traffic jam; being the first fine Sunday of the spring, everyone was down there by the river with their cars. We eventually got through by Charles yelling out of the window at every Tom, Dick and Harry about my condition. I felt rather conspicuous but was too busy coping with the breathing and relaxing in our springless Mini to mind.

Eventually we arrived at the hospital and they examined

me immediately. I was six centimetres dilated. I asked the midwife whether the baby was still lateral. Apparently it still was, and the head was still rather high, although I wasn't told this until after she was born. The Sister thought I would be there for about thirteen hours because of this. She was marvellous. She let Charles give me a bath after I'd had the enema (the thing I had been dreading most about the whole confinement) which I hardly noticed. Contractions were coming right on top of each other with only 30 seconds in between – very strong indeed. Sister was terribly nice. She brought me one of the other babies to see when I was in the bath to cheer me on a bit when I was at the depressed stage, and it certainly helped. I could hardly wait to see one of my own!

By the time I got on the delivery table at about 6.30 p.m. they were really right on top of each other, with no gap whatsoever. At that point I found it very hard to relax, although Charles was wonderful, breathing with me and wiping my face, and keeping on at me all the time to let myself go.

The breathing is *so* easy when one is actually in labour. It becomes second nature, and I couldn't have stopped if I'd tried. Sister was amazed, and when Dr. F. arrived she kept telling him to look at me and see how relaxed I was. She was amazed that I could cope with two-and-a-half minute long contractions with only 20 seconds at the most (more often five or ten) between them.

At 7.15 p.m. I felt the urge to push, but it had gone by the next one, so I left it, but told Sister, and she examined me and said that there was a very tiny anterior lip, but that I could push in about four contractions' time. Eventually I was told it was all right to push. That ten minutes transition, though short by many accounts, seemed endless, and it was then I felt I wanted either to be put right out and wake up with a baby or pack up and go home.

At 7.30 p.m. the second stage started, and it was simply *wonderful*. The contractions were painless when I really pushed so I started really pushing. The doctor and Sister and Charles could cope. He would just stand back and watch. I moved the baby down very fast and she was born at 7.50 p.m., twenty minutes later. I did not tear, and needed no episiotomy. Sister was particularly pleased with the actual delivery. I was in the left lateral position, curled up and looking between my legs so I could see what was happening. Charles saw the head coming down long before I did, as he was dressed up like Dr Kildare and was allowed to roam round the place and see the performance from all angles. He held my right leg up in the air so that I could see properly, and I saw the head crown.

I was able to obey Sister's instructions completely. I stopped pushing and panted when she asked, and we just eased Cressida's head out as slowly and gently as if it were a flower opening. It was a wonderful moment. She was pale mauve and yelling! The whole body came out with the next contraction and she was given to me for a minute, all wet and beautiful and screaming her head off.

I was given an injection after that by Dr F. to make the placenta come away quickly, which it did, about five minutes later. Then Charles and Cressida and I were left to ourselves for nearly an hour. I have never felt so marvellous as I did in that hour. I felt just like having a party and showing Cressida off to everyone I knew!

I have had absolutely no trouble with breastfeeding. She went to the breast the minute she was put there. My milk came in two days after she was born. I had one or two rather uncomfortable nights with engorgement. Cressida regained her birthweight in four days and never stopped putting on weight every day. I came out of hospital on the sixth day as I felt so well. My mother came to be a charlady for a week and she was really marvellous. She just did all the housework and washing and left the baby to me – never interfered or expressed any worries or doubts.

I feed Cressida when she wants it and she worked out her own routine by the time she had been home a week. She is a wonderfully happy, contented baby, and (of course) very, very beautiful, with a fine mop of blonde hair.

Thank you for helping to make everything so marvellous. I think of how ignorant and unprepared I would have been if I hadn't been to the classes, and shudder to think how much I'd have missed. As it is, Charles and I have a little girl we both helped to produce in every way, and the experience has enriched our already happy lives beyond all expectations.

IMPATIENCE

A long labour, or one that starts very slowly, has its own perils – not least that resulting from a gradual lowering of morale, a failure of nerve, despair, and maternal exhaustion. The woman in a long-drawn-out labour needs concentrated emotional support. Note that the appearance of the show does not necessarily mean that labour is imminent – only that something is probably going to happen within the next few days.

I have been meaning to write during the last three or four days but have so enjoyed the luxury of being waited on and feeding myself and the baby that I have done little else. This child is a first grandchild and great grandchild and much visited in consequence!

The course of events was as follows:

Wednesday evening the show began.

Sunday afternoon contractions at two-minute intervals shortening to five minutes by 10.00 p.m.

10.30 p.m. I rang the midwife to tell her of the situation, i.e. weak five minute contractions.

11.30 p.m. The midwife informed me I was three centimetres and gave me a drug to help me sleep a bit.

3.00 a.m. I woke, then dozed till 7.30 a.m., with still weak three minute contractions. Decided to forget about them and get on with ordinary living.

Mid-morning the midwife called, gave enema and bath.

3.00 p.m. Three minute intervals, still weak.

4.00 p.m. Rang the midwife to tell her of this.

6.00 p.m. Midwife came, and her pupil, reporting very slight progress. They gave more sleeping drugs at about 9.00 p.m.

3.00 a.m. I woke with much stronger ten-minute contractions. I coped with these badly till 7.00 a.m., when I woke properly and then coped well.

7.30 a.m. I rang the midwife who arrived and confirmed the improvement in outlook.

9.30 a.m. Hot bath, and the intervals shortened from then on and strength maintained.

11.15 a.m. I was examined and pronounced eight centimetres and getting on with it. Given 100 milligrams pethidine.

The contractions strengthened, relaxation improved, some confusion as result of the pethidine, but tiredness was relieved.

Very short transition lasting perhaps three or four contractions.

40 minute 2nd stage and delivery of 8 lb girl at 2.05 p.m. My main comments are :

I was from Wednesday in a state of ill disguised and ill controlled expectancy as the result of the show, and this gave way to pessimism as a result of the very slow and unworkmanlike beginnings of labour and general frustration with one's body. By Tuesday morning I was unwilling to believe the baby would ever come, and thrilled when pronounced to be really in labour. This was an immense relief and the rest of the time was immensely enjoyable, if strenuous.

Everything went absolutely smoothly. Breathing came quite naturally – also pushing. I was surprised, as I expected to be, by the strength of the urge, but enjoyed it and got three good pushes for most of the contractions. I wouldn't have had so much pethidine, but the advantage in my case of conquering fatigue far outweighed the disadvantage of some confusion. Gas and air I tried out of interest, but it was superfluous.

Over all, the labour was highly enjoyed by us both. Above

all I was thankful to be at home and not in hospital, and to have such a co-operative, patient husband and midwife.

For the first stage I was either ignoring it and moving about, or when I was concentrating on the contractions and lying down, I was on my side and having my back rubbed. In the second stage I was on my back, with my husband holding my shoulders and my legs held up by me and the midwife.

The baby was posterior, which would explain the unexpectedly long first stage, but she came out in an anterior position.

I should like to end by saying how much we have both enjoyed the whole process of pregnancy and labour, and the baby. I am busy refuting the attitude held by women one meets occasionally, who maintain that labour puts man eternally into woman's debt! What an idea!

B.B.A.[1]

*This mother had had a rapid but painful first birth and was
not looking forward to coping with labour. In the event the
labour looked after itself!*

Jessica was delivered at 3.30 a.m. this morning, by me all
alone, and poor Ian missed it all, being upstairs asleep.

The baby was due in a week's time – always an approximate date but I did not think it could be out by more than
about a week. For the last seven days I had had strong Braxton Hicks in the night, and frequent tightening ups in the day.
But I kept on hearing of people who had had twinges for
several weeks beforehand, so increasingly I became sceptical
of these as imminent signs.

Yesterday morning I woke at 3.15 a.m. with twinges that
actually hurt a bit. They were coming every five to ten
minutes, and after about four I got up to go to the loo, thinking to ring the midwife after. Twinges promptly subsided to
the Braxton-Hicks level of discomfort, and after sitting up
for three-quarters of an hour I came back to bed with a hot
ice pack and slept till morning.

In the morning I got up as usual and decided to go to
church since the contractions were very mild and not very
regular. While there the contractions stopped. I caught up on
my lost sleep during Ben's [her older child] midday nap, and
contractions did not start again till about 4.30. I was now
lying on a sun lounger in the garden (gorgeous day) and
knitting.

Contractions varied from mild (needing no special breathing at all) to moderate (needing my breathing level raised

1. Born Before Arrival.

98

just a little). They were not very regular, but averaged intervals of fifteen minutes. This went on till bedtime.

I came to bed at 10.30 and immediately they began to be painful. I think this was associated with the relaxation I was doing to fall asleep. Lying on my right side I got a sharpish pain during contractions from the baby's foot? knee? at the top left of my uterus. Lying on my back there was a bit of backache, so the left side seemed most comfortable, which was also the position you had recommended.

I was now caught in a dilemma. If I rang the midwife, I guaranteed no sleep at all for me and her and Ian. On the other hand, after my quick labour last time I ought not to leave it too late. I might not be able to sleep anyway. I did not know what to do and cried a little. I was scared because my labour had hurt so much last time. Ian favoured going to bed and trying to sleep. He was really tired. I needed him to help me through the bad bit still well ahead, and I didn't think he would be able to help me much if he had had no sleep at all. I decided to give sleep a try – at least those attending me would benefit. Now nearly midnight.

In fact I managed to doze a little between contractions. I also relaxed between them, and was still just able to meet each one in time to cope with it. I could not time them as the light was off, so instead I counted them. After eighteen (since originally going to bed, or thirteen since midnight) I put on the light. It was 1.30. I calculated that meant they were not yet coming at five-minute intervals. Ian mumbled in a sleepy way. Although he had said clearly that if necessary I must not hesitate to wake him, I thought I still needed him to have more sleep. I decided to wait till twenty-five contractions and put the light out again, to do more relaxing.

After the twenty-fifth I got out of bed quietly and came downstairs. I planned to call the midwife, but to let her examine me and do shaving and the suppository while Ian still slept. I went to the loo, and then lay on the spare bed in the playroom to calculate the interval between contractions. I was getting a bit confused now, because they were coming fairly strong. I was using mouth-centred breathing and now relying strongly on my attempt at a 'focused concentration' technique which was to gabble the Our Father silently through a contraction. One contraction took me through the prayer three times – which gave me a kind of way of knowing that a contraction would soon be over.

The next delay was needing to rush to the loo two or three times, where I had diarrhoea. Contractions were now getting rather confusing – they seemed to be often very short and rapid. I had still not had a show, so thought I could not be much dilated. Although contractions were most unpleasant –throwing out my breathing and relaxation – I still expected worse to come – the 'bad bit' of Ben's birth.

I got to the phone and sat on the sofa to ring the GP unit. My speech was quiet and strained but coherent. They kept on asking what seemed silly, lengthy questions. When did contractions start? What was my address? Was it my first baby? Of course these were not really silly questions at all, but I just wanted them to send me someone quickly. They said they would find out who was on duty and get her to ring me, so I should stay by the phone. It was ten to fifteen minutes before the phone rang. It was not my usual midwife, but someone else who I had not met. Again this daft question, 'When did contractions begin?' For simplicity I said 10.30, as I was not capable of explaining more, though I would have liked to. By now I could hardly speak at all – it is what I call the telephone pips stage of labour, because contractions were so thick and fast there were only a precious few seconds to communicate vital information before the next one was on me. 'Are you there on your own?' 'No' was all I could say, I couldn't explain that my husband was upstairs asleep. 'Oh, there go the waters!' as they burst out over the sofa. 'Is it your first baby?' 'Second. The first one was very fast.' 'It sounds as though you had better get to the hospital as soon as possible. I can't get to you all that quickly.' I wanted to ask what to ring for an ambulance, as Ian cannot drive, but I could not utter anything but moans and groans.

Then I felt the second stage was coming. Fortunately the midwife was still on the line. When I could speak I said, 'I think I'm going into the second stage.' She said, 'Put down the phone and I'll be with you as soon as I can.'

I put down the phone, and the first push came. As with Ben, there was no voluntary element in it – it just felt as though the contraction had moved down and was wrenching a new set of muscles into violent spasms. With the second push I felt the head had come through. I put down my hands, and sure enough, there was the baby's head already born. I felt great relief. The baby was really there, waiting to be born in seconds. I thought, 'I will just have to trust the cord is not round its neck,' but I did not feel alarmed, just confident and relieved. The third push catapulted the baby into my waiting hands. It was breathing. I lifted it over to see the sex – it was a girl. I held her to me, calm and happy. She was a bit spluttery, but seemed to clear her breathing herself more successfully than my attempts to tilt the mouth down. She was coated in vernix, and had quite a lot of darkish hair. I sat for five minutes or so, thinking, 'Is this real? Is she really born? Is my labour really over?' I though I would only be sure it was true if I got Ian to come and verify. He also needed to be up to let the midwife in, and the baby needed to be wrapped in something for warmth. I wondered how I could alert him without dripping my mess over everywhere, including the stair carpet and the new hall carpet. I stood, and as I did so a splash of blood and water fell out onto the sofa and the rug. I opened the door and called. He heard at once and cried, 'I'm coming,' and luckily Ben did not wake. I went back to the sofa and sat down, still holding the baby, with the cord linking her to the placenta still inside me. Ian came down and looked blank. 'It's a girl,' I said.

Ian brought a towel to wrap the baby, and ten minutes later he heard the midwife's car. 'Come and see this girl,' he said. 'The baby is already born.' The midwife walked in and said rather coolly, 'Doing me out of a job.'

As she went about her business, cutting the cord, injecting

101

me, deliving the placenta, clearing up mess, almost with an air of 'tut tut'. I said, 'I won't go into hospital now?' She said firmly that that depended on the doctor, who had to suture my tear.

When she came to ring him she turned out to be on my side: 'I don't see why she should go into hospital – they are both well. No I don't think it can wait several hours. No, I see no need to send her in, and she doesn't want to go.' Eventually he agreed to come and stitch me up if the midwife would get the suturing kit from the hospital. She rang her pupil and sent her. It turned out that Jane – the midwife – had had only one hour of sleep, and had an induction at 8.00 that morning. She gradually thawed and was very kind in clearing up the mess.

I was glad you had told us what to do in such an emergency. I think all antenatal classes should include such simple emergency instructions as that you do not need to hold the baby up by the feet and that you should not try to deliver the afterbirth yourself, but just wrap up the baby and wait for help.

Although I did not do it on purpose, I could not be more delighted at the way it turned out. Not only do I feel very clever for delivering my own baby, but I avoided going into hospital with all that I dreaded about that. No strange, clinical atmosphere, no institutional rules, no separation from Ben with the strain that would put him under, no disturbing him in the middle of the night to leave him crying at someone else's house, no frantic ringing of doorbells and throwing stones at windows to wake them up. Just peace and rest and calm and autonomy in my own home, with the best possible conditions for Ben's acceptance of the new baby. I would not have chosen a home confinement because I know there are risks, but I am so happy it worked out that way by accident.

AN AMERICAN GIRL RETURNS HOME

This mother attended classes in England and had her baby in the States.

I would love to help other women have the enjoyable preg-nancy and birth I did. When I thought of having my baby here I asked the doctor about Steve being with me for de-livery. His reply, 'I wouldn't even want to be with my wife.' 'And when,' I asked, 'do you bring the babies to their mothers?' 'After three days. You're too tired before then.' So off I went to Washington. The doctor there was encourag-ing, but more *surprised* by our success.

The chance I took there was that Steve wouldn't be with me. But the day before I was due I had backache and spot-ting. Steve arrived on the next plane. I went into the doctor's office for a checkup and they sent me to the hospital. At noon Steve and I were left alone in the labour room – a private room with its own bathroom and TV. The doctor checked periodically.

Two hours after I arrived they broke my waters to speed things up. I had already dilated four centimetres, but I hadn't felt any contractions until then (2.00 p.m.). Soon your book began to come alive. Everything worked perfectly. For the first two hours after induction the contractions were easy and five minutes apart. Steve read me helpful passages from your book.

At about 4.00 p.m. I had to work harder at the breathing, and moved up into shallow chest and mouth-centred breath-ing. Once I felt myself withdrawing from the scene – I turned my head to the wall and curled up. Steve leaned over, counted, and breathed with me, and I emerged.

At about 5.15 p.m. I began to have the urge to push. What a beautiful, powerful sensation that was! No one will believe there was no pain then.

At 6 p.m. we went into the delivery room – small and very personal. Stephen, the doctor, four nurses (two curious students) and I. Getting on the delivery table I felt less than agile. My feet went into stirrups, but they didn't tie me at all. Steve was at my head, and he did all the talking then and was my main support. The panting for pushing was perfect and I had two pushes. At that point the doctor said, 'Please stop pushing until I get my gloves on. I want to have some part in this.' One push and Jessica's head came out. What a gorgeous baby she was! Two hard pushes for the shoulders. Steve was as proud as I was. 'I'm so glad we did it this way. I really feel she's ours.'

And when she was in the nursery for the first twelve hours her record card read '9 lb 7 oz. Excellent Natural Child-birth!'

THE DOCTOR TOLD ME TO HOLD HIM UNDER THE ARMS AND PULL HIM OUT

This mother's baby did not engage before she went into labour. She was very short, and it looked as if there might be some problem with the descent of the baby through the maternal pelvis. Unfortunately the hospital, excellent in other respects, does not permit husbands in the labour ward. The doctor who did the forceps delivery helped her to join in and actively give birth to her son.

At last it arrived! First let me thank you very much for all your help and encouragement. We are very happy. I am afraid I did not do everything according to plan, but even so what I learned at the classes was invaluable, and I would certainly recommend every future mother to go.

On Wednesday I went to antenatal clinic as usual, and after observations the doctor decided not to let me go over the time as the baby was getting rather large (my weight was stationary) and with my past history of high blood-pressure, one kidney,(1) etc. So on Friday I was admitted to hospital to be induced on Saturday. However they were very busy with emergencies so I was only started on Sunday at 12.30 p.m. Just before, I was shaved and had a hot bath, but no enema. Had pethidine injection and membranes were ruptured. Then was put on dextrose + ? drip and very slight contractions started. (They were about the strength of the trial ones I had been having lately.)

2.40 p.m. Bruce came to visit, and in the meantime they

listened to baby's heart and took my pulse every half
hour

3.45 p.m. Bruce had to leave. The drip was increased, as
there was very little change in contractions. Passing
water regularly.

4.20 p.m. One minute contractions. I had ice-cream and a
cup of tea. I felt rather warm but comfortable, and was
breathing well, and relaxed.

4.45 p.m. Contractions about the same with one-and-a-half
minute interval, but not very regular.

5.05 p.m. Contractions 50 seconds long – irregular.

6.10 p.m. Rectal examination. Shallow chest breathing over
peak of contractions.

6.30 p.m. Contractions coming in groups of two or three
strong and then mild. Two to three minutes between
groups.

7.15 p.m. Offered injection but refused, as I felt quite well
and was coping very well with the contractions.

8.00 p.m. Occasional very strong contractions which needed
mouth-centred breathing with the odd deep breath.

8.20 p.m. Slight nausea.

9.00 p.m. 55-second contractions every one-and-a-half
minutes, very strong, with backache. Drowsy but coping.

9.15 p.m. Vomited. Contractions as before, but have been
unprepared once or twice.

From now on I was not able to keep notes at regular intervals. However I think I remember most of it in the right
sequence.

The contractions got stronger but the intervals and length
did not alter. The backache got steadily worse. I tried to
relieve it by going on the side, but contractions were very
uncomfortable other than on the back propped up. Nurses
helped with massaging. Had vaginal examination – three
fingers dilated and stayed that way for the rest of the night.

I asked for light pethidine injection provided it did not put
me to sleep! Told it was too late, and was given gas and

oxygen instead. It helped, but the mask itself worried me.

Time seemed to go very slowly with nothing happening to show for it. Began to feel very weary. They decided to give a small dose of sedation after all, which helped me to regain strength. In the meantime the composition and fastness of the drip was increased to get my contractions to come more frequently, but this had very little immediate success.

Early in the morning had another injection and another vaginal observation, during which the doctor attached an electrode (2) to the baby's head plus others to me, as they wanted to keep an eye on the baby as labour was getting rather long. Contractions did finally get stronger and closer, and I just wanted it all to stop and didn't even want the baby any more! I was able to relax between contractions. The doctors and nurses were very helpful – and to my surprise they even complimented me on how I was coping, despite my thinking I was *not* coping at all. Somebody said, 'It shows you went to classes for relaxing and breathing!'

Eventually at approximately 1.30 to 2.00 p.m. I was taken to the delivery room for vaginal observation, but, if found fully dilated, they would help the baby to come out by forceps, as things were getting rather drawn out. The cervix was virtually dilated, so they helped that last bit.

I was locally anaesthetised, given an episiotomy, and the forceps were inserted. I was fully conscious throughout, even if a little drowsy, and I must say I enjoyed this part of it. During the pushing I had cramp in my thigh, but the nurses rubbed it well and it was soon gone.

The actual delivery was wonderful! There seemed to be a purpose to the contractions and the pushing, and in three contractions the head was out, and then a little hand with long, thin fingers. It was a lovely feeling to see it all. It was 2.35 p.m., about twenty-six hours after induction.

I followed the midwife's instructions for pushing – and I remembered to relax my mouth, and anyway I could not help smiling at this strange, hard lump moving down. The doctor told me to hold him under the arms and pull him out for a cuddle on my tummy. He whimpered as soon as the head was out, and it was very thrilling. He was bruised and I felt very sorry for him and found myself crying! They took him away to tidy up the cord and suck the mucus out. Then, wrapped up, I had him to hold again for a little while. He was then taken for a rest.

The placenta came out quite easily with a little push and tug, and I was then sewn up. No problem, even though the anaesthetic was wearing off.

Blood was taken for matching up with the baby's to see whether I might need the injection for antibodies, as I am Rhesus-negative. (I did have it on Tuesday, so all will be well with the next babies.)

I was then left on my own after a cup of tea. In no time Bruce turned up dressed in a gown and mask, and sat by me in the middle of this large ward. I was very tearful but very happy, and wanted to kiss Bruce (something of an impossibility through a mask!) After he left I was tidied up and taken to the maternity ward, where Bruce saw me again about 6.00 p.m.

Crispin came down cleaned and weighed at about 10.00 p.m., but was taken again for the night as I needed my rest. In fact they are taken out for the first four nights. After that they are always with the mother. It is a very nice ward. Crispin's swelling (3) and bruising is going down fast, so I hope he will be looking more normal when he has to meet the world outside! He is now breast-feeding very well, even though my milk is not in plentiful supply yet. He seems contented though, and has not needed top-ups.

Notes

1. She had had three attacks of TB, and had a tubercular kidney removed.
2. This is a tiny monitoring device which can be placed on the baby's head through the partly dilated cervix.
3. The swelling on the baby's head, fairly common after a really difficult and tedious labour, was due to being pressed

down against the cervix before it was fully open. It is a bit like a large blister, and the baby's brain is not affected in any way.

HUSBANDS NOT ALLOWED

In the following two accounts a husband and wife analyse their feelings, and the conflict aroused by not being allowed to be together.

She wrote:

Here are James's and my accounts of our/my labour. James's is incomplete as he wasn't allowed to be with me, but it may be of interest to you as a point of view from a well-informed father who *wasn't* present, and as a comparison with the accounts of other, luckier fathers.

I had a fairly quick and comfortable labour and really enjoyed it as long as I was fully conscious of what was going on. I was given two doses of pethidine, which rather knocked me out. However this wasn't till the very last minute.

The baby himself is an absolute darling. I realise James and I are biased, but everyone has remarked how lovely he is. He was 6 lb 13 oz.

His story:

I am a heavy sleeper, and when Anna first got up in the early hours of Tuesday morning, complaining about having backache, and wanting to go to the lavatory all the time, it didn't register to me as being anything but one of those occasions when Anna got up in the middle of the night. Anyway, it was nearly two weeks before we needed to start getting apprehensive, so I didn't think this was a sign of labour beginning. And perhaps, in view of the fact that we had some relatives (mine) coming to visit us in the evening, I didn't want to know. Anyway, we got up to have breakfast about 9 – I was due to start work at 11 – both of us doing a

110

bit of preparation for it in the normal way, but Anna not wanting anything but toast and coffee in the end. It must have been during breakfast that we realised that Anna's pain was coming and going and so could it possibly . . . ?

So, laying aside the newspapers, I timed the intervals between them and they turned out to be about five to six minutes apart. It looked very much like the real thing, amazingly enough, and not just some annoying ailment that would make Anna grumpy today. (I think that thought was pleasing.) So I decided I had reason enough for not going to work, and phoned up at about 10.30 a.m. to say I wasn't coming 'as my wife appears to be in labour'. Of course the breathing exercises were in full swing by now – though they still did seem like exercises – and from time to time I made a note of the intervals between contractions, and the length, thinking perhaps the information may be of use later. Anna's worries seemed to be twofold : she wanted to finish an article for the magazine, as planned, today, and she wanted to stay at home as long as possible so that she didn't have to wait a long time in hospital. And as we were pretty certain I wouldn't be able to stay with her in hospital for the birth, it was obviously best to stay in the flat together while we could.

So, for a while, Anna sat on the sofa, typing at a low table and regularly stopping to breathe through a contraction, as I looked on, occasionally telling her to blow, when I thought it necessary – about the one thing I could remember from our last talk with Mrs K., only a week before. I was at the other end of the room most of the time, tidying my desk and sorting out some bills; I also went out to the post box round the corner mid-morning and to do a little shopping nearby. While I was out, I met our downstairs neighbour; I told her about Anna and she told me how she had had a false alarm labour a fortnight before the real thing. This of course set me wondering . . .

Soon after, I seem to recall, I got some coffee and we decided over it that they were getting a bit stronger : this was no false alarm. I rang the hospital and was told 'Bring her in

111

when she feels like it; let her have a meal if she feels like it.'
All very vague; so we were staying put for the time being.
But, at about one, when Anna had finished her typing but
didn't feel like a meal, we got her things together. I got some
ice cubes in a Thermos (not used, as it turned out), paper, an
apple and anything that might possibly be needed (for me)
for a long wait in the hospital, and we went down to the car
for the short drive to the hospital. There was no feeling of
panic at all. Possibly the weather, which was grey, cool and
unexciting, helped a lot in this. Thank God it wasn't hot, as
we'd feared.

Once we'd got there – and it was quite a long walk along
corridors to maternity – we eventually found a nurse who
got us organised. Anna was led away into a tiny room to
change ready for examination, and I was left feeling faintly
awkward at the corner of a corridor by a liftshaft. When
Anna was left alone, I sneaked back to have a word with her
and see how her breathing was getting on, but when the staff
nurse came back, I was sent scuttling guiltily away again.
Clearly men were regarded as in the way from now on. After
I had gathered together Anna's clothes and things to be taken
home, it was clear I was no longer needed. I tried to tem-
porise, saying I wanted to be sure that Anna wasn't going to
be left alone in labour, but a nurse assured me this wouldn't
be the case – although she annoyed me with the tone she
adopted, as if I were a worrying husband who didn't know
a thing about what was happening.

So away I went, in my confusion not even saying goodbye
to Anna, to go back at 3.00 p.m. – visiting time. Back at the
flat, things were a bit tense naturally, and I fear I was a bit
hostile to my mother-in-law and Anna's youngest sister, who
had turned up – possibly because I resented any one but
Anna and myself being involved in this event at this stage.

When I got back, at 3.00 p.m., with Anna's mother, Anna
was just, we were told, going into the labour ward. I had a
fleeting glimpse and then was sent downstairs to wait anxiously, in the typical manner. I sent Anna's mother away, and

then found time hanging heavily, with only the *Daily Mirror* and *Woman's Own* to read, and only scraps of non-information coming through from the labour ward upstairs. Finally, at 4.30 p.m., the sister came down, spoke first to the mother of another girl who was in labour at the same time – tension thus mounting – and then asked me to come up and see my wife. I asked what had happened but she simply said 'wait and see'. I had to put on a white coat, thinking in my confusion, perhaps I was after all to be present at the delivery. But when I got in there was a baby! And Anna lying there, exhausted but happy-looking. I asked her how she had got on and then went over to see this strange new creature who had suddenly materialised. He looked like any picture of a newborn baby, but he was ours! But I hadn't been there with Anna when he'd come, and I felt that I had let both him and Anna down.

Anna's story: 'a tremendous sense of power'

Our baby, Timothy, was born eleven days early, so the whole thing came as a bit of a surprise. Even when his head was straining against the birth canal with every ounce of my energy, I still couldn't quite believe that it wasn't a false alarm, and that I'd be able to get up, go home, and start again later!

Labour began at about 4.00 a.m. with me getting up to go to the lavatory with what felt like constipation. I slept on and off till about 8.30 but had to get up a couple more times. This feeling of wanting to empty my bowels persisted throughout labour. Even at the height of the Big Push, I was sure that if only they'd let me get up and go to the lavatory, everything would be alright!

By the time I'd got up and had breakfast, the contractions were coming every five to eight minutes and lasting about 45 seconds. I breathed my way through them, rather enjoying myself – It still seemed like practising. During this stage, I finished off a feature I was writing for a magazine – I was determined to do that, whatever happened. Then I pottered

113

around, made some phone calls, had a cup of tea, chatted to James and our downstairs neighbour, packed my case, and tried to decide if it were the real thing or not. James phoned the hospital at about noon and the nurse said, 'Bring her in when she feels like it.'

Finally, when contractions were coming every three to four minutes and I couldn't concentrate on anything in between them, I decided to go, at about 1.00 p.m. The hospital was only up the road and we got there between one contraction – breathed through while sitting on the garden wall, to the curiosity of some passing workmen – and the next. My only tearful moment came as we entered the foyer; I blubbed to James: 'I don't like going into hospital.' (I had been hospitalised for abdominal operations twice before.)

In the maternity dept., I was undressed and shaved, and then James, having lingered as long as possible in the hope of being allowed to stay, was regretfully sent home and told to come back at 3.00 p.m. I was given an enema, spent about half an hour sitting on the loo, which satisfied even my doubts about my bowels (when the mucus plug came away) and then had a blissful hot bath in which I nearly fell asleep between contractions. All this time I had been breathing through the contractions with no trouble, and explaining to the Staff Nurse, who was preparing me, what my operation scars were for in between. When I got out of the bath, at about 2.15 p.m., they were getting really strong. (An odd thing I noticed was that the nurse referred to the contractions as 'pains', which irritated me – to me they were just contractions.)

After that, things moved quickly – and nearly left me behind. I was expecting to lie in the ward next to the delivery room for a couple of hours, breathing away. The nurse said: 'Let me know when you feel the baby is pushing down the back passage', and the next thing I knew, he was. So up I got and walked into the labour ward and clambered on to the bed. I asked for my first shot of pethidine at this stage – about 3.00 p.m. – as the pains – in my back – were getting a bit excruciating, though not unbearable.(1) With the second

114

shot, about fifteen minutes later, which I didn't ask for, I went off into a kind of drunken stupor, which I regret. However, I was able to arouse myself when necessary and interrupted the nurses' conversation with a peremptory: 'Here comes another one' or 'Hold my foot please,' or 'Can someone hold my head up.' If James had been there, he could have done these things for me, and would also have encouraged me to be more awake, I think. As it was, the drug seemed to release rather hostile feelings towards the midwife and nurse for not allowing him to be there, and I even took a perverse delight in not pushing when they were telling me to. I had negative rather than positive feelings, which probably slowed the labour down.

I certainly wasn't at all inhibited emotionally in the labour ward, and called variously on God, James (several times), and the baby – to get a move on. 'It's no use you telling the baby to get a move on,' the nurse reproved me. 'It's you who should be getting a move on – come on, push!' 'I *am* pushing,' I roared, so loudly they must have heard me at home.

I suppose there must have been about twenty of these monumental pushes, in which I felt as if my whole body was converging on to the birth canal and trying to get out through it. And then, suddenly it was over. I opened my eyes and there was the little blue bottom slithering out into the midwife's hands, trailing the blue cord with it. Suddenly I was completely aware: 'Oh, baby,' I announced, and sat up to get a good look at it. It cried, but this didn't touch me as much as the sight of the little bottom, perhaps because 'the first cry' has become a bit hackneyed – I knew it *would* cry. The first thing to make sure of was the sex and if it was all right – it was a boy and he was. I took hold of the midwife's hand and apologised for making such a fuss and she said I wasn't nearly as bad as some they'd had, which was comforting. (Talking to other mothers later, this seemed to be true.) I lay back, quite relaxed after the midwife had cut the cord; she gave me an injection to bring on the placenta, and removed it when it came. I was just allowed to put my arm round the

115

baby before he was whisked away to be washed, weighed, measured, etc. I had a small cut and tear, so a young woman doctor came in to stitch me.

At last James came in. It was about 4.30 p.m. (The baby had been born just after 4.00 p.m.). He looked very awed and abashed and chokey in a long, white coat. We were very pleased to see each other, though I was feeling distinctly woozey still. We both sat looking at the baby, who was stretched sleeping in his transparent perspex cot.

He was really beautiful; his skin was all peachy and glowing, not red and wrinkled at all. His face was full of character, with a tiny cleft chin like his father and a wobbly mouth like some of my family. I kept saying to James, 'He's ever such an attractive baby, isn't he?' I felt rather in awe of him. We'd seen the film *Kes* the night before and it had been all mixed up in my thoughts throughout labour. In one sequence, the boy hero explains to a sympathetic teacher the relationship between him and the kestrel he has trained: 'He's not a pet – I haven't *tamed* him . . . I get the feeling he's only letting us look at him as a favour.' I felt like that about the baby. Now I've got to know him better and had him at the breast, he's not such a stranger. But that was my first reaction – the feeling that the baby was challenging me: 'Here I am, a new life. You brought me here; what are you going to do about it?' At that moment I had no idea of the answer.

I think the classes helped me immensely. Firstly, looking back on the labour, I am able to understand clearly nearly everything that happened. Even at the time, I was able to understand my own reactions, and to analyse them later – I wasn't surprised at any of them, thanks to the thorough preparation and foreknowledge our discussion in class had given me. The breathing exercises certainly helped me to cope. I really enjoyed the early stages of labour, and felt thoroughly in control as I typed my article and got ready to go to the hospital. I feel now, looking back on it, that I did have some grip on the situation in the delivery room, even in

116

my battle of wills with the midwife. When I did a really good push, I felt a tremendous sensation of power and determination, though I think there were fewer of these '*good* contractions' than there might have been because I wasn't alert enough to go with them in an all-out effort. However, as soon as it was all over, I was sitting up and taking notice. The whole thing seemed to have been very casual in a way – I was wearing one of my own shortie nighties, and I had it on all the time during the delivery and no socks or anything else. And I kept the same nightie on that night – it hadn't got dirty or stained at all. In the maternity ward, I heard lurid accounts of pools of blood but I don't remember anything like that.

I was very glad I'd been to the classes, mainly for the understanding and enjoyment they'd given me, and for the relaxed and happy approach I had in pregnancy right up to the last stage of labour. I never at any time, in the whole nine months, felt fear. My only and permanent regret is that James wasn't with me to share the experience and to help.

Several girls in the maternity ward said that they were glad that their husbands hadn't been there after all, as they'd found it such a harrowing experience. But I believe my husband knows me well enough not to be shocked by excessive emotionalism – and he certainly knew what to expect physically. In the limited part he did play, he was a great help. In the early stages of labour, he methodically timed my contractions and made a note of them. He helped me finish off my various tasks and made a note of the things to be done, not getting in a panic at all. We chatted to each other, and he made tea for me, and finally, when things seemed to be moving fast, he drove me off. He explained to the nurse what I was doing with breathing, though to her credit, she could see for herself and said I was doing very well. He also reminded me to blow, which I found very helpful. He seemed to remember Mrs K.'s instructions more clearly than I did, and again, this would have come in handy during labour when I forgot the push/stop pushing/blow technique. In fact, I found blowing – a kind of quick-pant/blow routine (2) – helped me over the height of the strong contractions better than the straightforward mouth-centred breathing.

He finally left me when I'd been shaved, but I found his support and reminders invaluable up to then, and his mere presence a tremendous comfort. Despite the midwives' justifiable desire to get on with the job without having amateurs around, I believe that they are mistaken to deny a woman this comfort which would, in the end, make their job easier.

Notes

1. Again, notice that women use words in very different ways – 'excruciating' – but 'not unbearable'.
2. This would need watching if the mother did a lot of blowing over a number of contractions, as it may result in over-breathing and consequent hyperventilation of the maternal blood stream. She flushes out too much carbon dioxide, and this can have the effect of actually cutting down the oxygen supply to the baby. Unprepared mothers often do this in the stress of the late first stage of labour.

THE SECOND BABY – AFTER A DISTRESSING FIRST BIRTH

Lilian had come to me because she was dreading her con-
finement, and the re-enacting of suffering she had endured
during her first labour. It was almost too much for her to
face, and sometimes, especially in the middle of the night,
she was in a state of terror.

My baby, a lovely little girl, was born in the early hours of
yesterday morning after a labour of only three and a half
hours! I'm overjoyed with my little daughter, and so thrilled
that everything went so well. I woke at 12.30 a.m. with a
contraction, and from then on things never stopped happening! The contractions came thick and fast from the start –
so much so that I never had time to look at a clock and time
them! My midwife had told me to call her as soon as I was
sure I had started, as she said second labours were often
short after a previous forceps, so Mike phoned soon after
1.00. Time seemed to go so quickly as I was occupied with
getting organised before Miss G. arrived and having a bath
after she came, but this all taking a long time because I had
to keep stopping in mid-action to cope with a contraction.

In a way it was trying, to have so little respite between contractions, but on the whole I think the frequency and my
activity between them were good in that I hadn't time to
think; I just *had* to keep pace and stay in control. During the
first stage I only felt moments of panic with about three contractions, and never completely lost control, and I certainly
found the breathing a tremendous help. I didn't need to use
mouth-centred breathing till very near the end, and I found
it easy to sustain the rhythm.

119

Miss G. examined me internally when I had finally got bathed and said, 'That's amazing. I'm sure you're fully dilated. Do you want to push yet?' For the next couple of contractions I thought I did slightly, and then the urge really came – an amazing experience, quite terrifying in a way, but so exciting, and apart from the first one when I couldn't quite get the breath-holding, I think I managed pretty well to do effective pushing. (I felt that I was instinctively doing what my body demanded.)

The really overwhelming part was when the baby was really well down in the birth canal. The contractions and the completely unfamiliar feeling of this huge object, apparently in my rectum, meant that my immediate reaction was that this was something alien. I can well understand why some women 'hold back' there – but I remember telling myself, 'No, this is wonderful. My baby's nearly born. I mustn't hold back.' I was also feeling that I would be badly torn, but between contractions I told Miss G. of any worries like that, and she was very reassuring and helpful. She told me the head was visible to encourage me, so Mike showed me in the mirror and what a thrill to see the dark diamond shape that was showing! I can't very clearly remember the details of the last few minutes (the whole second stage was 25 minutes) but I had one contraction when I just couldn't seem to push. I said this and Miss G. told me not to worry, it might be better for me not to try and push now, the baby would get pushed out anyway. Soon after that I looked down at the end of a contraction and there was the head – I hadn't realised that it had actually been delivered, and I was so excited then, and I followed Miss G.'s instructions to give a little push, stop, and pant, feeling her manoeuvring like anything, then suddenly saw that marvellous little grey-pink body held up in the air and almost at once showing signs of life! What a marvellous feeling of joy and achievement, like nothing else I've ever experienced!

Mike was really glad to have been with me and to see his daughter born. He gave me just the support I needed, but as things turned out this was very little as I don't think I was ever in danger of 'giving up', which was something I was afraid might happen, as I am far from courageous about pain! In fact both Mike and Miss G. said that I'd appeared to them to be quite in control. I'm delighted to say that Miss G. was most impressed by my handling of the labour and was sure that the breathing helped to keep the first stage short, as I obviously wasn't impeding the activity of the uterus, and she said that it was unusual, in her experience, for anyone to go through a complete labour without a need for some help from drugs.

The sessions with you helped me to get rid of a lot of fear and apprehension, and Mike felt that he was really geared up to playing his part. It really does feel marvellous to have succeeded in something so challenging, especially after the bad experience of my first confinement. One last factor, very important for me and, no doubt, for most women, was being attended by a midwife who was so very understanding, interested in me as an individual, and whom I really trusted.

FIRST BABY AT 39

This baby weighed 9lb 9oz.

First of all, hats off to the medical profession, I was very impressed by the skill and genuine interest of all the doctors and nurses. St M.'s is marvellously modern – husbands are encouraged to participate as much as possible and it was excellent, all except for the food – which was ghastly!

I was brought in rather early as, until the last moment, they were prepared to do a Caesar if necessary on account of my former operation (1) and my age (39).

In the event I was able to have a vaginal delivery, albeit with forceps. The waters were broken by the doctor on Monday evening, and the baby arrived Wednesday night. It seemed a long time in between! I couldn't eat and only wanted sips of ice water – and as I was sick a few times I was put on a dextrose drip. However – I breathed my way through the contractions without needing any other help. I was asked if I wanted anything, and I said at that point I was fine. Later the midwifery tutor, to whose classes I had gone twice (saw a demonstration bath) came in to see me. Our class were all downstairs and she was *very* impressed with my breathing and said she'd go and tell them all!

The baby arrived with the doctor and me both doing all we could. That pushing takes a lot out of you – but it *is* a marvellous feeling afterwards. I had a lot of stitches, and was able to talk about a mutual friend with the doctor during all this! My husband was then allowed in to see the baby – naturally he had been asked to wait outside with the need for forceps. A wonderful moment of achievement! The baby was cot nursed for 48 hours. We are trying to sort out the feeding – she seems still to need a supplementary bottle – but I hope we can manage fully to breast-feed.

Already Abigail is terribly precious and we are deeply grateful to God for giving us this gift and responsibility.

The classes were a tremendous help. Keeping the palms upwards and simple things like that make an enormous difference . . . Birth is an amazing experience!

Note

1. Two years before she had had her baby Mrs M. had an operation for fibroids of the uterus, and had one ovary removed.

A LIVING BEING –
WARM AND WET FROM THE WOMB

The mother writes:

I had come into hospital on the previous day to have the baby induced, as it was over two weeks late. I had been given castor oil and an enema, and told to wait. I waited – until 2.00 a.m. Then I woke from a good sleep with low backache. I wondered: is this it? It was!

My back was really quite painful, but I was able to massage it myself, and able to doze a bit. At about 4.00 a.m. I was aware of the first contractions starting. They seemed to come every ten minutes or so, not very strongly, certainly not strongly enough to tell anyone about and so disturb the whole ward. So I continued my back rubbing, breathed with each contraction, and dozed on and off. At the 'official' waking time – 6.00 a.m. – I told the nurse, who called the Sister. I was asked whether I wanted to stay where I was, with company, or go to the labour room on my own. I opted for the labour room, and asked the Sister to call John and ask him to come along. By the time she phoned him, it was 6.50 a.m.; he had some breakfast, at my suggestion, and arrived at about 7.45 a.m.

By this time I was having stronger contractions more frequently – at about four minute intervals – although they varied a bit. My backache was still uncomfortable, and John massaged it and the inside of my thighs, which helped a great deal. The contractions became stronger, but still varied a bit in time, and, on the whole, I felt perfectly able to cope. John, unfortunately, had to give a lecture at 11.00 a.m. – the only time during the whole week when he could not get a stand-in!

– and I asked the Sister to examine me before he left so that we had some idea of how far things had got. This she did, and seemed surprised to find that I was already between six and seven centimetres dilated, and had not yet asked for any pethidine. I just hoped that the baby would not arrive in the hour that John was away.

In John's absence a student midwife took over the massage of my back – not nearly as effective as John's massaging – and stayed with me the whole time as the ward was not at all busy. I also had a hot water bottle in the small of my back, which helped. Also during John's absence the doctor came to see me, examined me, and said the baby was still in a posterior occipital position, and would probably rotate on its own (which it did later on). I was advised to lie on my left side, as this would help the baby to rotate; it also made rubbing my back a lot easier for John. The nurses kept asking whether I wanted pethidine, and if not why not. They were all fascinated by my 'method' and kept looking at the book. One nurse particularly was keen for me to have pethidine, but I resisted her pressure, and she realised that I was serious. Barley sugar and wet flannels were both tremendously helpful and are to be strongly recommended.

John came back soon after 12 noon; things had not altered very much, although contractions were stronger and more intense. I was not yet doing the shallow rapid breathing, as I felt I could cope without it, and although some of the stronger contractions were uncomfortable they were far from being painful. It was soon after John got back that I had my first 'show' and the nurse then said that the waters would break shortly. I suppose my idea of 'shortly' was not the same as hers, and I got a bit impatient at this stage! On the whole, I felt I was controlling my breathing all right, although every now and then I was caught unawares, and lost the rhythm.

At, I suppose, about 1.00 p.m. or perhaps a bit before, the Sister said she would take me into the delivery room. I was beginning to feel the urge to push, and although not yet fully dilated, she thought the delivery room was the place for me at that time. So off I went, followed by a stream of nurses and midwives – and John.

Contractions were now very intense, and I was beginning to feel that mouth-centred breathing should be brought into use. The urge to bear down was terribly strong (I had no idea it would be as strong as that) and without John there, keeping me 'under control', I would have lost my breathing completely. He reminded me to blow out when I felt the urge to push, to breathe rhythmically, and to be patient – a thing I found difficult! I found it incredibly difficult not to push when I had the urge, but the blowing out helped. I did not find it easy to relax my legs, and they felt a bit cold in spite of long white socks. The midwife said she wanted three hard pushes with each contraction: the contractions were now very close and intense. The feeling of the head on the floor of the perineum is a strange and difficult one to describe: it was like a ball coming through an opening not quite large enough, and falling back each time to try again and this time to get a bit further. It wasn't painful: certainly it was uncomfortable, but no more than that. It could also be likened to a wave washing up on the seashore, coming a bit further each time. I got, I realise now, a bit impatient. I think this was partly because the midwife said the waters had not yet broken, and I knew they must before the head crowned, and partly because she and John could just see the head appearing, and I couldn't . . . As it turned out, the waters drained away unnoticed, but I kept expecting them to come with a sudden burst, as the midwife said they would.

I had by this time been turned on to my left side from lying on my back, as the midwife said this would be easier for delivery. Although I didn't know it at the time, she did an episiotomy and the head was born very soon after. It was thrilling: I saw the rest of the baby being born with two more contractions which came very easily, and although her first cry was a second or two later, it seemed like hours. She had had the cord twice round her neck, and it had to be cut after the head was delivered. Her first cry was the most thrilling sound imaginable. The most welcome cry one can ever wish for. The nurse wrapped her in a blanket, and gave her to me, and the joy and happiness which she gave to John and me in just those few minutes was something which we shall treasure for ever. I was hardly aware of the placenta coming away: John and I were overjoyed by the birth of our first born.

Certainly it was a tremendously exhilarating and exciting experience, and one which could not be the same without one's husband there. I could not have done it as I did without John's help, love and encouragement. He kept my breathing under control. It made childbirth a pleasure instead of a horror.

Labour had lasted almost exactly twelve hours: Rosalind was born at 2.10 in the afternoon. The experience for both John and me was a very moving one, one which we'll never forget. I couldn't have done it without any analgesics if he had not been with me. His help, encouragement and love were constantly present, and the joy of all three of us being together immediately is indescribable. Immediately after the birth (I felt I wouldn't mind doing it all again on the next day – or perhaps two days later) I had to have stitches, during which time John waited. I felt absolutely fine, wanted to rush off and phone grandparents, and felt terribly exhilarated. Unfortunately the doctor found that I had a tear high up in the wall of the vagina (because of a narrow birth canal) and, after long discussions with the gynaecologist, they decided that I should have a general anaesthetic for the stitches. And they couldn't do it for an hour and a half, and wouldn't let me phone as it meant going to one of the wards and they were afraid of infection. So they kept me in the delivery room. As a result of the anaesthetic I felt much more groggy that evening than at any time previously. The after-effect of the anaesthetic, and then, the next day, the stitches, were by far the most uncomfortable sensations during the whole process.

Once in the ward, nurses kept asking me about my 'method', and about a dozen student midwives were brought

127

in on the following day to have a demonstration of breathing, and ask questions about it. And it seemed such a pity, as new patients came into the ward, to hear them all discuss their various labours, the agony they went through, how glad they were that it was all over, and how dopey they felt all the time with trilene. It all seemed so unnecessary.

The birth of a baby is surely something which should be shared by both its parents. To be fully conscious and aware of what is going on, not stoically accepting pain but actively helping the baby to be born, is the right of every mother. To suffer the birth of a baby alone, without your husband, and not feel the joy and love which should be felt between them at this time, seems wrong. To see this helpless little baby which they have created together emerge into the world must surely enrich and strengthen any marriage. For us, it was a tremendously moving and rewarding experience, never to be forgotten.

It took a bit of time to get used to Rosalind. She seemed so small and fragile. I am breast-feeding her and this seems to agree with us both. She grows fatter almost as you watch her. Although a lot of work, she is a constant joy, and we love the idea of parenthood. It was a wonderful experience for us both. I shall try to encourage natural childbirth wherever I can; I think it's wonderful.

The father writes:

I awoke at ten to seven; quite definitely *before* the phone went, but literally only a few seconds before. The Sister said Jane was having 'good contractions at about five-minute intervals' and suggested that I have some breakfast and come along to the hospital. I got there at ten to eight and found Jane in a side ward, looking relaxed and happy.

The next three hours went terribly quickly: contractions came at slightly varying intervals, but generally every four or five minutes. I spent most of my time massaging Jane's back and giving her barley sugar sticks to suck.

128

I had to leave at 10.45 a.m. to go and lecture, and as Jane had not yet been examined, the nurse arranged to do so before I left. She and the midwife were evidently very surprised to find how far advanced Jane was in the first stage; she was already six (seven?) centimetres dilated and they clearly expected her to be making more noise and writhing around. They do not often see 'Natural Childbirth' practised in this hospital, and were very curious and all took turns reading bits of Sheila Kitzinger's book.

Jane's breathing was still fairly 'low down'. She 'rode' most of the contractions well and rhythmically, except when one caught her unawares. She did not vary the *pace* of her breathing quite as much as I thought she was supposed to. She lay on her back and found massage of it and of the insides of her thighs most helpful in coping with the contractions comfortably. While I was away a student midwife took over the massage (the ward was not very busy).

I returned from my lecture at 12.10 p.m., and found the position much the same. Jane said the nurse's massage was less good than mine. The contractions were more irregular and intense, and the waters had not broken, which Jane seemed to find uncomfortable. But the baby had rotated itself naturally (no doubt helped by Jane lying on her side) into a normal position from the posterior-occipital one.

The waters continued to be a problem. The 'show' came soon after noon, and everyone said 'the waters will come out with a plop'. But they did not, and in the end the midwife said they must have drained away bit by bit.

Soon after the midwife came back from lunch she said that as Jane was beginning to feel the urge to press down and was fairly well dilated, she should be moved into the delivery room. I donned, with the others, a mask and coat (Emergency Ward 10). It was at this point (1.30 p.m.?) that Jane seemed to be at her most uncomfortable; breathing was not so well controlled: often a 'catch' which she herself denied was due to the transitional stage of labour but said was because she had got her breathing out of phase; and she had particular difficulty in relaxing her legs (even though she had woolly stockings on and pillows underneath). She was lying on her left side for at least an hour before moving into the delivery room.

In the delivery room Jane did get hot and valued cold flannels to suck and to have on her forehead. The second stage took about 40 minutes; before the head crowned the midwife did an episiotomy. The baby was born very quickly then and the cord was cut at once because it was twisted round the baby's neck. The time was 2.10 p.m., almost exactly twelve hours after Jane felt the backache which preceded her first contractions (which started at about 4.00 a.m.).

Jane was given the baby. I was standing behind the bed and found this a wonderful moment. Jane had had no analgesia throughout and looked relaxed and wonderfully happy: all her mind concentrated on this little creature, and her arms reaching out lovingly for it. This is a time for husbands to value and treasure, of tenderness and fulfilment.

Jane continued in high spirits and happiness. I can see why some husbands would not enjoy their wife's labour. But what they miss! The feeling that one can genuinely soothe, help and encourage one's wife and share the climax of the birth seem to me to deepen the warmth and understanding of a marriage.

As for the baby, I was frightened by it. Such frailty: the paper-thin, yet powerful, cry. A living being, warm and wet from the womb, utterly helpless, bemused, staring about with bright eyes. Tiny fingers and fingernails plucking at the air. Perhaps it is a sense of responsibility that frightens me, or some primeval feeling of guilt. I have helped to create a life; a pulsing being that might be crushed sooner or later in a million different ways: a small accident, an illness, in a cataclysm. Yet the baby having been born one feels its journey is ended, not just begun. That it should suffer the risks of life seems unfair. Before this tiny presence those risks seem

130

formidable. One is acutely aware of the preciousness of a life. One drives with extra care this day. One sees people about one as more real people.

A DISAPPOINTMENT

Some women feel that they were out of tune with their bodies in labour and look back on childbirth with regret. Perhaps it could have been better; was there anything they did wrong? They often went into hospital far too soon and then over-active management by interventionist obstetricians has contributed to the uncoordinated experience of a labour which, slow to start, was then augmented and became too much for the mother to cope with so that she felt completely 'out of control'. This is then followed by drugs, which too often have the effect of sedating and confusing the woman without providing adequate pain relief. Commands to push and to 'try harder' and 'keep at it' further contribute to the labour in which there is a frustrating sense of psychosomatic unco-ordination, and the woman pushes desperately because everyone is urging her to even though it feels all wrong. This invariably means that she is bearing down at the wrong time and that instead of concentrating on opening up she is putting all her energy into athletic effort and so becoming exhausted.

Sometimes, too, women have very clear ideas of how labour 'ought' to be and when a particular labour is different and difficult believe that they must somehow have 'failed'. This is an entirely inappropriate way of trying to measure the experience of childbirth; labour is not like an exam which must be passed. It is an intimate personal psycho-sexual experience which is composed of a wide range of mingled positive and negative emotions like the high and low notes and sharps and flats in a piece of music.

Tanya felt deeply depressed after the birth of her 'strong, alert son' and felt that she had to 'come to terms with' the experience of birth. Two weeks after delivery this is what she wrote.

At 7 a.m. awoke to find slight leaking of the waters. Felt excited and nervous – a little doubtful at first of whether this was in fact liquor. Told Jay, and from 8 a.m. (when mild, irregular contractions began) we began to look forward to the day and development of labour. Had a leisurely breakfast. Next, I phoned my obstetrician who advised that we 'slowly wend our way' to the hospital.

During the morning – light show, continued slight leaking of waters and frequent, painless but by no means regular contractions. Jay went out on about an hour and a half's business during the morning (calling me every half-hour for a report!) whilst I enjoyed intensely sitting in the sun-filled lounge listening to lute music, reading and sewing a kaftan – no feverish spring-cleaning urge for me, although I did do some light last-minute chores.

We lunched at 1 p.m., aware of its possibly being my last opportunity to 'stoke up'. Felt nervous by now yet was not keen to 'submit' myself to the hospital too soon. But at 2.30 p.m. when Dr B.'s secretary phoned and asked in a mock-stern voice why we were still at home I became more anxious to obey doctor's orders.

We arrived at the hospital about 3.30 p.m. It was a beautiful, unseasonally warm day and the world looked fresher and lovelier than usual during the drive.

After routine procedures (forms, shave and enema) I joined Jay and we settled into our allotted labour/delivery room. (I had been surprised and encouraged – falsely? – that during 'prepping' nurses had said my contractions felt quite strong to them, and couldn't I feel anything?)

Until 7 p.m. – walked about, read and sewed. We tried timing contractions now and later but at no stage did they seem to assume a regular, gradually-accelerating pattern. I think that at this stage I felt slight impatience and disappointment – as it wasn't happening as in the textbooks!

The obstetrician arrived at 7 p.m. to assess progress and decided to accelerate labour by means of pitocin tablets. Things certainly started taking a more decisive turn! For two and a half hours I took the tablets whilst we played draughts and chatted. Contractions continued irregularly but became 'busier' though perfectly tolerable, with just occasional need for deep chest breathing.

At 10 p.m., when contractions suddenly became stronger and demanding I was found to be two centimetres dilated. This sounded like poor progress to me but in no time labour rapidly took on fast-moving and overwhelming proportions! (Here the tablets were discontinued.) From this time on I was on the bed, lying on my side(s) in the position learned in antenatal classes.

It seemed there was no time between contractions to consider any other possible positions. Indeed there was clearly no time for relaxation or really controlled breathing, as the beginning and end of contractions were indistinguishable. Jay's repeated attempts to introduce some form of relaxation and calm to my handling of this 'tempestuous' situation were rudely brushed aside by me as I was overwhelmed by yet another wave. I voiced my fear that I was 'not coping as I should', asked for sponge, then massage, then water, then sponge and at the same time could not for a moment tolerate losing his presence and constant touch! (Poor Jay was kept on the hop but coped wonderfully.)

I was behaving in a way which belonged to the transition phase, yet this seemed to last the whole of my active labour (10 p.m. – 12.15 a.m. and then when expulsion began too). I was quite overwhelmed by the physical turmoil but cannot recall it as real *pain*. It was an intensely turbulent, annoying, confusing and powerful 'animal' sensation. I grasped desperately at breathing patterns and put them into practice in some wild, untidy manner! Firm lower back massage was very comforting and I recall having felt the need to stroke the perineum myself, with some relief.

At some stage I vomited an apple eaten a few hours earlier

– I had had a dread for months of nausea during labour! – and at the same time my nose started bleeding and had to be plugged from time to time. 'What a sight I must look', I thought. The sister gave me an anti-nausea shot, and then at about 11 p.m. came the regrettable offer of 'something to take the edge off the pain'. This was 'Omnopon' – obviously prescribed by my doctor – though I vaguely requested a half-dose of pethidine. (I did not, in fact, want or intend to accept any such drug but presumably resisted only feebly and Jay must have felt I should have relief. I don't believe that this injection brought much relief and am sad that it left me extremely 'woozy' – so that after delivery I had to *struggle* to remain in touch with my beautiful, calm babe, my husband and doctor. The discomfort would have been preferable to the relief (if any) and unpleasant drowsiness. At my post-natal visit I discussed this point with my obstetrician and we agreed that next time the question of pain relief must be more specifically settled *before* labour commences!)

Time in heavy labour seemed to pass rapidly. At about midnight I felt strongly the need to bear down but the sister was reluctant to permit this or examine the cervix until Dr B. arrived. Upon my insistence of about ten minutes she finally examined me and found full dilatation. I began pushing and Dr B. soon arrived. When I sat up for the expulsion stage the waters suddenly broke – gushing out in a satisfying way! (The earlier leaking was of hind waters.)

Now – friends and books all say that pushing is the most pleasing, satisfying part of labour. My experience wasn't so. I know that a strong, perhaps painful sensation is felt against the rectum and that one should bear down 'beyond' this. I tried to give the impression that contractions ended sooner than they really did because I so dreaded another push or two. (Needless to say, I fooled nobody!) There honestly was little or no 'pushing *past* the pain' and I suppose I was surprised and angrily disillusioned at this. Apparently I was pushing well, yet had absolutely no awareness of progress (a mirror would have been helpful). Pushing lasted about 40 minutes and I simply wanted to sleep or escape!

Jay and I were anxious to adopt, as far as possible, the procedures of Frédérick Leboyer at the birth. We had the empathy and interest of our obstetrician who, for this reason, wanted to avoid a forceps delivery. As Tristan weighed 8 lb 14 oz and had a largish head it was essential, I'm told, that either an instrument delivery or a generous episiotomy be performed. (Despite my optimistic hopes of perhaps escaping an episiotomy – I got one!)

Dr B. playfully threatened to rattle his instruments at me if I didn't push effectively. This helped me renew my waning efforts and eventually at 1.05 a.m. our baby was born. He seemed suddenly to 'appear' between my legs – a quiet, beautiful little being. (I was regrettably unaware of the exact moment of birth – was this the result of local anaesthetic given for the cut or of my generally drowsy state? But what a pity I couldn't feel his body 'slip out' as so many mothers describe this precious moment.)

Delivery of the placenta followed immediately (perhaps because of immediate suckling) and, strangely enough, was the most pleasant sensation up to this point! The soft, warm object passing out of the vagina was a soothing and sensuous feeling.

The period following the birth was extremely significant to us and we were thrilled at having Leboyer's techniques applied as faithfully as possible under institutionalised circumstances. I could have appreciated those first 30 minutes so much more had I been fully 'awake'.

To summarise then:

I should, I think, have preferred a slower, 'orderly' labour to the fast and furious one I experienced. Was acceleration necessary in my case? My doctor tells me it was.

I should also have liked to do without so-called pain-relief and its awful after-effects.

I felt disappointed and a little humiliated that, with all my preparation (physical, emotional and intellectual) I seemed to cope inadequately. Of course I *do* wonder repeatedly how much more inadequate my 'meeting' of the experience would have been had I not read, exercised, discussed and thought.

Finally I realise that no two labours are the same and that therefore there can be no 'textbook' labour! (i) My contractions were completely undefined, running into one another to form one lasting, intense 'menstrual cramp'. There was no interval between them during which to relax or gain control over the situation. (ii) Pushing was not the pleasurable, relieving activity I had expected.

I realise that, despite the disappointments, the birth was 'normal' and we have an awful lot for which to be thankful and happy. But nevertheless . . .

I WATCHED ENCHANTED AS MY BABY'S HEAD
EMERGED

*The husband was brought up in a Mediterranean country.
For him it was a matter of masculine honour to have nothing
to do with what culturally was 'women's business'. He was
at first highly amused at being asked to help his wife with
exercises during her pregnancy, but turned up for a private
consultation – and gaily accepted the task. Although he had
intended not to be with her during any part of labour, when
it came to the birth day he was away from her for only the
two contractions which preceded delivery.*

I was feeling awful on Tuesday. I had a bladder infection –
with chills, fever, and the first backache of my pregnancy.
Went to the G.P. mid-afternoon for the infection and he said
that the backache might be early labour.

At 1.00 a.m. Wednesday I had a 'show' and vomited. I
was dismayed at the thought of starting labour after being ill
all day, and decided to go back to sleep and think about it all
the next day. But within an hour my husband and I decided
to check with the hospital, as the contractions were about
three minutes apart and lasting from one to two minutes. We
packed a suitcase and, convinced that we were going on a
false alarm, set off for the hospital.

Contractions now were strong enough to be sure that they
weren't just baby kicking, and I began to feel excited. At the
hospital I was taken upstairs, shaved and examined, all the
while handling the contractions with ease. The midwife put
her hand on my belly and said, 'You must have taken classes.
I can always tell.' The staff doctor (mine never arrived) said

that I was eight centimetres dilated, and she burst the membranes. I was then moved to the labour room for an enema (didn't do too well with that). Oh – incidentally, for my whole labour I was lying on my side in the foetal-like position I have slept in throughout my pregnancy. Lying on my back seemed unappealing at the time.

The midwife (a cheerful darling) came to tell me that after the enema the contractions would prove too hard to handle and I should take an injection. I assured her that I would if I needed it – and she went away happily to fetch my husband. The two of us were alone for the next six contractions – contractions which I found fantastic! Each was closer to the following one than the ones before, and each consisted of three or four peak bearing-down sensations. During these six contractions my uterus took over, and I marvelled at its tremendous power. The sensation of enormous pressure at the back passage might have alarmed me if I were not prepared as I was. I found these contractions overwhelming and thrilling. The sixth was different in that I felt as though something 'gave' – as if a cycle was completed. I thought that the baby must have passed the cervix, although I couldn't feel it in the birth canal. I told my husband to run for the nurse. I asked if I could be examined again, and she replied, 'When the doctor feels it necessary, she will examine you.' The midwife was right behind her and said, 'Let's have a look, luv.' She took a quick look and yelled for a wheeled bed. In a flash we were tearing down the corridor for the delivery room. I had a rather weak contraction, during which she did an episiotomy because baby's hand was by his head and he was coming quickly. She told me to push on to the next contraction. I gave a most gentle push and watched enchanted as my baby's head emerged. The next contraction and another gentle push and his lovely little body slid into the world. 'Oh, it's a boy' I breathed. I almost swooned with joy as he was placed on my belly. He was perfectly beautiful, and yelling and warm. The afterbirth came with the next gentle contraction. I had been at the hospital less than three hours. The doctor stitched me while the midwife weighed Nicholas. – 9 lb 7 oz. My husband came in and we joyfully admired our son. This birth was one of the most wonderful experiences of my life.

MOZART AND FORCEPS!

Becky has been born! She arrived at 4.53 a.m., weighing 7 lb 2 oz, wide-eyed and looking very much like my husband. She is a darling and contented little baby. Before she was with us 24 hours she already felt like the most natural person to have around, and very much an extension of our 'completeness'. Although at that first amazing sight of her and in the next minutes after, it was impossible to comprehend that she had truly come from us.

The waters began leaking at 8.00 a.m. with about seven or eight mild, irregular, vague contractions during the day. I felt tired, unbelieving, not excited.

Nicholas taught his classes.(1) Contractions with a bit more focus about the cervix (at last) started at 7.15 p.m. at fifteen-minute intervals. We were itchy, so we played Mozart and Schubert four-hand (the Mozart in particular stayed with us right through labour and all the morning after she was born). Contractions, still generally unconvicing, were coming at seven- to eight-minute intervals by 11.00 p.m. so we checked with E. (the obstetrician) and he said, 'High time'. I felt rather silly going into hospital with very mild contractions at 11.30 p.m. because that wasn't my idea of labour. When they got to be three to four minutes apart I finally got that 'clever' feeling, because the levels of breathing were practically spontaneous. The contractions were short but somewhat painful, but they felt *good*, while I thought 'open' and 'down baby'. By about 2.00 a.m. contractions were about two to three minutes apart, perfectly handleable. I lost track of certain time then, but the next phase contractions were one-and-a-half minutes apart, sharp but manageable, but rapidly after that, painful. Finally the contractions began

141

taking on a form nearer to that which I had expected, that is the uterus seemed to swell up, then close down, while the cervix and back seemed to tighten around the baby's head. Mr E. checked me then before going home for a rest (I was his second that night) and said to the midwife that the contractions were excellent, that a decompression suit couldn't produce better ones. I was six centimetres dilated. Nick, of course, was a dear, his presence and physical touch absolutely essential. He warned me when I was due for contractions, rubbed my thighs and back, reminded me to smile, relax, breathe. The midwives from the beginning kept remarking how relaxed I was for my first baby, how well I was handling contractions, and was I sure I didn't want anything? Unfortunately when I took to high chest breathing the chief midwife kept telling me during contractions to breathe deeply and that she just didn't know about this breathing business. That discouraged me. But Nick and I, seeing that I was coping much better at upper level, decided to go back to it.

I was trembling wildly all over. The contractions were really rather wicked, and Nick knew before I would admit that I would need help. (Nick's main concern for the event was that we would stay in touch, which we did, and mine was that it would be an enriching experience for us.) It was hard to decide anything. My memory seemed to be fifteen seconds long. I kept hoping that I could make it to second stage and then all would be better. I was noisy – poor Nick – and I finally said that I wanted a caudal. When I finally had it I was furious when I learned that I was fully dilated and could 'push any time' (4.00 a.m.). However Mr E. found out that she was transverse, which explained better why it was difficult, and I realised that because of that it would have been an assisted delivery after all, and that I had probably done all that I could. Mr E. rotated the baby and let me push – rather ineffectively. It finally occurred to me that my shoulders and head were flat down and Nick lifted me. That helped me, but the foetal heart was 108, and Mr E. neatly cut

142

me and then delivered her by forceps. Nick could see step by step. I asked him what he saw. He said 'the head . . . the shoulders . . . just as in the books'. Then I saw her too, all at once. I shouted and broke into a kind of tearless, joyful crying, still trembling, but now with pleasure. Oddly, that the baby had a sex hadn't occurred to me, and when Nick said, 'It's a girl' I only said, 'Oh, is it?' I just couldn't tell what it was like for Nick; but that afternoon he said it had been a very exhilarating experience, and a positive and successful handling of it, possible only with the classes.

Note

1. The husband was a university lecturer.

THE WAY A HUSBAND CAN HELP

This mother suffered from very severe asthma which did not diminish or disappear with pregnancy – as it often does. She was worried as to how she could possibly breathe her way through labour and whether she would not very soon become exhausted and breathless.

I didn't do it all myself. Mr Y., the consultant, decided on a forceps delivery as he didn't want me to get done up too much on account of my asthma, but I had an injection and was fully aware of proceedings throughout, and Chris was with me for the whole course of labour, other than the forceps delivery and sewing up afterwards. He was absolutely *super*, and we're both so excited and happy, to have our little boy, to have had the experience of giving birth to him, and to have coped.

I kept my labour log book from the rupture of the membranes at 7.00 last night until about 4 o'clock this morning, when I went into transition and both Chris and I were fully occupied in dealing with contractions; and I wrote it up from memory as soon as I was brought up to the ward this morning.

It seemed to be straightforward, easy and uncomplicated. The membranes ruptured at 7.00 p.m. and my sister ran me out to the phone box, where I warned the hospital I'd probably be in at some time during the evening. I had the first contraction – like a very mild period pain – at 7.40 p.m. and contractions continued very mildly and at varying intervals throughout the evening. Miriam cooked us a meal of smoked haddock with cheese.

9.30 p.m. on. Contractions regular at five minutes intervals, more mild than some Braxton-Hicks! I was coping easily using only deep chest breathing. We settled by the fire and listened to Alfred Deller and Mahler on the gramophone.

10.10 p.m. on. Contractions at four minute intervals, lasting about a minute.

11.00 p.m. on. Three-minute intervals, lasting about a minute.

11.30 p.m. I had three running which necessitated shallow chest breathing, so we decided to go into hospital.

12.00 midnight. I arrived at hospital, contractions at three-minute intervals lasting about a minute, and some needing shallow chest breathing. I had a bath, during which the lights went out.

1.40 a.m. I had two injections – hydrocortisone (which was most useful) and pethidine (the consultant thought I ought to get some rest). I really didn't feel I needed the pethidine, but, on the other hand, I did get some sleep between contractions from 2.00 to 4.00 a.m.

Chris said I breathed through them in my sleep!

I asked for ice cubes and got them! Chris says contractions were at two-minute intervals, lasting a minute.

About 4.00 a.m. Contractions at two-minute intervals, lasting 60–80 seconds and sometimes running into each other. I was just able to cope, starting with one deep breath and then going to shallow chest or mouth-centred breathing direct. Decided I must be in transition. Chris rubbed my back, stroked my hair and told me how well I was getting on, and, in fact, kept me in touch completely. I was terribly confused mentally between contractions, and sometimes talked nonsense to him. I was conscious of talking nonsense, which was disconcerting. Contractions were by this time quite painful.

5.30 a.m. Felt a tentative desire to push, but managed not to because of an anterior lip. Otherwise I was fully dilated.

5.45 a.m. Felt violent desire to push, but couldn't quite get the hang of it. I was just getting the hang of it when they decided to give me a pudendal bloc (1) and forceps. Pudendal bloc helped immensely, as the contractions were still pretty painful. I was getting two to three pushes to a contraction, and the midwife said I was doing well. They told me I'd need an episiotomy, and I said need I? Couldn't I just try harder? And they said I was trying hard enough and the consultant didn't want me worn out. The forceps/episiotomy didn't hurt a bit. They told me when the head was born, and I got immensely excited and saw the rest of him delivered. They let Chris in immediately afterwards and we held him.

He is a very alert baby already – follows everything with his eyes and tries to turn his head to follow a noise.

It was, I think, a pretty short and easy labour, and I really enjoyed some of it, and felt well in command of things except between about 4.30 and 6.00 a.m. I couldn't possibly have managed, though, if I hadn't learnt the breathing and relaxing, and if Chris hadn't learnt to be so magnificently calm and confident and soothing. The midwife was most helpful and kind, and, apart from a couple of examinations and some most acceptable encouragement, left Chris and me to go our own way.

Note

1. This involved injections in the perineum which anaesthetise the birth outlet, but nothing else.

CAESAREAN BIRTH WITH AN EPIDURAL

We have two adopted children who are seven and five and suddenly found after trying for nine years that I was pregnant. We were thrilled! Towards the last month or so of pregnancy the baby was breech and then transverse and back to breech again. The consultant suggested that I have an elective Caesarean. I must admit I was taken aback at first. A Caesarean had never crossed my mind.

I am 33 and having not been able to conceive for all these years we didn't want to take any risks. So we thought about it and prayed about it and decided that this was probably the right decision if the baby remained breech. I had a scan and the week before my due date I went in every day for a CTG reading to keep a check on the baby's heartbeat. I found this was a fantastic experience, it allowed me to get acquainted with the hospital and there was something about going in each day and hearing the baby's heartbeat, it set off the preparation for what was going to happen! It was really a special time.

Because it was probably going to be my only pregnancy I hated to give it up. It was as if it were going to be a special separation for me, and for my whole family really. We all cherished it. My boy and girl would come in while I was in the bath and watch the baby move and we had such a warm feeling about the baby before it was even born!

I met the anaesthetist. This is the key to the whole process. She prepared me and told me exactly what to expect. She also warned me that at any time she might have to put me out if I was panicky. She and the surgeon were very happy to do the procedure this way for me ...

There dawned the most beautiful autumn day and as I

opened my eyes that was my very first thought: 'What a fantastic day this is going to be! And it is going to be my baby's birthday!' It can't describe how euphoric I felt. It was a wonderful time and I think a lot of it was the preparation leading up to it. I was on the CTG machine that morning and turned it up so that I could hear the heartbeat and had very tender feelings about this baby, very protective feelings, like 'I know what is about to happen to you and you don't!' It was a very precious time . . .

They wheeled me out on the trolley in my little shower cap and gown and it was like a 'bon voyage' party. I kissed my husband goodbye at the doorway of the operating theatre. This is the one drawback. We were very disappointed that my husband was not allowed to be there. We had been through the classes together and were as prepared as anyone could be for the operation. I feel we are mature people. We both feel that he would have conducted himself so that he would not have interfered with the surgery and we know of cases where the husband has been allowed to sit at the mother's head in a rocking chair talking to her and can then rock the baby while they are stitching her up. It hurt my husband when he saw people pouring out of the theatre to feel that he hadn't been allowed to be there.

One of the girls from the antenatal clinic, a midwife, came and she said, 'I'm here, I'm here!' You could tell everybody was grinning behind their masks. Their eyes were full of joy, I was made to feel so cared for and protected. I must admit that I gulped as I went through the doors and suddenly was shaking all over from nerves and tension, probably fright. My one thought was, 'Oh if my legs won't stop shaking they'll knock me out completely.' Everyone introduced themselves to me and told me what they would be doing. They put a drip in. Then they did the epidural. It was just like you would have an ordinary labour epidural except that it had to be effective higher up. I curled up into a ball and one of the nurses held my hand the entire time. She talked to me and explained what was being done. She said, 'Do you mind if I call you Daisy?' and I said 'Heavens no'. It made it really nice, it wasn't a formal atmosphere. She really talked me through it. I concentrated on the breathing I had learned at N.C.T. classes at this point too. I thought. 'In just a few minutes I'm going to have this child that we want!' and it was such a joyful time.

The anaesthetist put the catheter in after a local anaesthetic so I had no discomfort from that. The worst part of the whole operation was the shave! Once the epidural took effect my legs stopped shaking. They put a drape over my chest so I couldn't see the operation. I was looking straight up at the lights and the whole time the anaesthetist was talking to me. She put a light oxygen mask on me and I was grinning. She said, 'What is it?' and I said, 'I can't believe it. This is glorious! This is so exciting!' I grinned through the entire operation.

I had specially tender feelings for this baby, especially knowing that this was going to be a sudden birth, not going through the normal birth process. I reached down and patted my stomach just before it was started and the anaesthetist said, 'What's wrong?' and I said, 'I just want to say goodbye,' and the next thing I heard the obstetrician say was, 'I'm cutting into the uterus'. I felt some muscular pulling and once they had cut the uterus there was a sucking sound. This is very similar to the suction apparatus they use at the dentists. Then they started to get her out and because she was breech she came legs first. The other surgeon was pressing down quite forcefully on the head to push her out and he said, 'These are long legs!' and then he said, 'It's a girl!' Words can't describe what I felt to be awake at the moment of delivery. They checked her over at my shoulder level so that I could see and they gave her to me to hold on the delivery table. I kept saying, 'Don't let me drop her!' and then they took her out to Andrew so that he could hold her.

All I had seen of the operation was a red thread coming up and down as the obstetrician was sewing. I did see him at one point holding something, I don't know what it was, and

I said to him, 'Make sure you put it all back, whatever it is!'

They took me to the recovery room and we were both in such great condition that we could then go straight to the postnatal ward. That is another advantage, that you don't have to spend time getting over an anaesthetic. Immediately Andrew was brought in and we were with him.

I didn't feel any pain. It was just a gnawing sort of . . . I wouldn't even say discomfort. I was so excited I wanted to get started on everything. Once the actual work is done you just want to get up and get out.

I felt terrific! When the epidural began to wear off there was a band of pain across my stomach which was the normal Caesarean discomfort. They had left the epidural tube in so they topped me up. The pain was high up on either side, a muscular pain. I wasn't comfortable lying on either side. But I was able to come home on the eighth day. I don't know whether the reason I felt so marvellous was that I didn't have any general anaesthetic, but I didn't have to go through all those exercises for coughing up that you have to do after general anaesthetic. When you try to cough you feel as if your insides are going to fall out, so if I had had to cough after the anaesthetic I think this would have been awful.

The midwife from the clinic came and held my hand and talked about how beautiful the baby was, what a wonderful experience it is and how exciting it had been for everybody.

If I could pick out one word to describe this whole experience it would be *joy*.

LIKE A HUGE ATLANTIC WAVE

Day before. Stretched at clinic. I did the pear (1) exercise to relax the pelvic floor and had a painless ARM. That night had Braxton-Hicks and mild pains.

7.30 a.m. Labour begins, fifteen-minute intervals. Deep chest breathing.

8.30 a.m. I decide that labour is sufficiently established to go into hospital. Dressing is difficult as standing seems to bring a mini-contraction.

9.30 a.m. Ablutions etc. Sister instructs a pupil on fixed and engaged heads. This head rocking set off hard contractions at great frequency. Wheeled off to my room. Shallow chest breathing as frequency drops to six minutes.

10.30 a.m. Wheeled to labour ward. I see prepared cot, which is encouraging. Three-minute intervals now. Battery of aids; shallow chest breathing; iced water on sponge seems to release all muscles – marvellous! Light hot water bottle on lower abdomen very comforting. I find shoulders now tend to tense up. I managed to relax them by rubbing them on the bed, like our dog on the Persian carpet. I scrunched up my shoulder blades, and then relaxed my shoulders, and the rest of my muscles followed. I held my palms upwards. It helped relax my shoulders during shallow chest breathing and between contractions. I had ice to suck during the intervals. Mouth-centred breathing was an unqualified success.

Gradually contractions lengthen and become less gripping and almost mesmeric. Like a huge Atlantic wave rising to a crest and subsiding, then flattening out to move into the next. Then, half an hour later, as more amniotic fluid flows out, the contraction abruptly changes, and as if the wave is breaking on my back and pushing me into a sitting position, I wanted to bear down. I managed to blow this away whilst Bill went to find the midwife. The second contraction came as I was halfway between the bed and the delivery bed. I was transfixed. Notwithstanding, the head was now at the perineum.

The third was more orderly. Mr L. said, 'Push,' and I counted to ten and then gave a small push. The head appeared, and then the shoulders, it seems in no time at all. The little girl was handed to me wrapped in a blanket, still covered in vernix, but gazing steadily at me through two large wide open eyes.

Note

1. i.e. she bore down slightly while feeling herself opening up below.

PEACE OF MIND

Katrina was very worried about having her baby, and particularly about having things taken out of her hands in such a way that she did not have control over herself. I think she felt that analgesics might somehow cause a mental disintegration. From her teens she had been in and out of psychiatric hospitals suffering from severe depression, had had problems with drug addiction, and was now slowly climbing back through the love and support of her husband.

From about 6.00 p.m. I felt a little discomfort from contractions and from rectal pressure. I didn't bother to time contractions as it didn't occur to me that the birth might be nearer than expected. The discomfort was probably greater then because we were in the tube, and although I felt I would be more comfortable standing up, it would have looked most odd to keep bobbing up and down there! The only thought I had was that the head must be pressing well down on the cervix.

At about 7.30 p.m. while we were having a meal I realised that the contractions were more frequent and regular. I asked David to time them for me. He became irritable doing this as he thought I must be trying him out for B. day! However, we found that the contractions were coming every two to three minutes and lasting for one to one and a half minutes. I did not need to do any special breathing then, but I felt more comfortable if I stood up during a contraction and rested my hands on the table so that I could relax my body from the waist downwards. At 8.00 p.m. I had a show. Then it hit me that this must really be 'it'. However, it was really very difficult to grasp the fact, as one doesn't expect a first baby to

153

come ten days early. We both felt very excited then, and laughed a good deal.

Between 8.00 p.m. and 11.00 p.m. the contractions were still coming every two to three minutes and lasting for one to one and a half minutes, but they were much stronger then. I didn't lift my breathing up much at first, because I thought that it must still be very early and I didn't want to tire myself. However the contractions became uncomfortable, so I went up to shallow chest breathing, and this relieved the discomfort completely. (At 10.30 p.m. they called the midwife).

At 11.00 p.m. the midwife examined me and found that I was five centimetres dilated and the cervix was very thin. The baby was presenting L.O.A. The midwife shaved me and I had a quick shower. This was uncomfortable, as I had felt more relaxed lying down. When a contraction came I stopped washing and put my arms round David's neck so that I could lean on him and relax a little more. Having returned to the bedroom, I found that I had to rise to mouth-centred breathing. The midwife remarked that I was using the breathing well. My legs then began to shake uncontrollably. Although I knew that this was a sign that things were moving fast, it was, I think, the most unpleasant part of the labour.

I felt that I had absolutely no control over my legs. The midwife told me to do deep, slow breathing between contractions, and this did help to lessen the shaking. At this time I was also sick. I suppose that we had the famous 'last meal' too late! Also I got a little cramp in my calves, but with massage this went quite quickly.

At about 12.30 a.m. the contractions were much stronger and I was feeling less relaxed. The midwife then told me to do transition breathing. I didn't feel that I wanted to push and so I was a bit surprised, but the midwife said that I showed signs of wanting to. I found that blowing out hard was a tremendous help and seemed to take away all the abdominal sensation. I must have been a little too enthusiastic about blowing out as I got a slight tingling in my fingers.(1) I used this breathing for about four contractions.

At 1.05 a.m. the midwife ruptured the membranes with her finger on examination. She didn't say that she was going to do this, and both the pupil midwife and I jumped as they broke with a pop. The midwife then said that I was fully dilated and that I could push with the next contraction. I was so surprised to hear this. Although I had been doing transition breathing, I don't think that it had really hit me how near the second stage must be.

I found that the pushing was really hard work, much harder than I had imagined that it would be. The pupil midwife and David were on either side of me and they supported my legs during each contraction. The midwife got me to hold my legs up with my hands under my knees. I found that it was a great effort to lift and then lower them after a contraction. I spoilt the pushing during the second contraction. I think that for a moment I must have been frightened. I then realised that I really had to enter completely into each pushing effort. The pupil midwife wiped my face with a cold flannel between contractions, and this was very refreshing. Throughout the labour I was fully alert and we were chatting between contractions. The feeling of the baby moving down the birth canal was very peculiar; I cannot say it was pleasurable, but only that it was quite unlike anything I had ever known or imagined. Sometimes I felt that I couldn't manage as many pushes as my uterus demanded, and I found myself doing mouth-centred breathing instead. The midwife said that that was a good way for a baby to be born. For most of the contractions I pushed three or four times. As the head came down lower the pupil midwife held a mirror for me to see. The midwife herself told me how much of the head she could see after each contraction. She was very good, and didn't tell me to push more than I felt my body was demanding. All during the second stage David kept encouraging me, saying that soon our baby would be born. I felt I wanted to say that I knew that, and didn't need reminding.

Just before the head crowned the bulging of the tissues

appeared so big that I was amazed, even though I had seen films and pictures previously. I then felt great pressure around the anus. At 1.35 a.m. the head crowned; this was very sudden and took me by surprise. The midwife told me to pant and I did this immediately. I then received the only drug I had during the whole of labour – the routine 0.5 mg. syntrometrine. The baby cried when only the head was out. The body then tumbled out immediately without any further contractions and without any pushing from me. I just gasped in amazement at the speed at which things happened, and with awe at this wonderful little being which David and I had produced.

I had expected him to look very blue for a few moments, but he didn't. He was just the normal baby colour. Afterwards the midwife told me that babies born to trained mothers were rarely blue, as the mothers breathed so well for the baby to get enough oxygen.

The placenta came very quickly at 1.40 a.m.

I held Jonathan straightaway. I then felt very shaky with excitement and I was sick again, and I also had some more cramp in my legs. I had no tear to the perineum.

I had always thought that I would want to put the baby to my breast immediately I held him, but I did not want to. I think that it was my own reaction to all that had happened. Afterwards the excitement came out in physical form. However I fed him about an hour after he was born. He weighed 6 lb 4 oz.

After cleaning up, the midwives left us together. They had made the birth of our son a wonderful experience. We couldn't sleep that night. We were so happy and so excited. I had to keep looking at him in the cot to convince myself that I wasn't dreaming.

My memories of labour are not of unhappiness and pain, but of really hard work in the second stage. At the time my only thoughts were to get on with the work which had to be done and to do it as well as possible.

The classes were very helpful, and we enjoyed the husbands' and wives' evening, and the film. All this assisted us greatly.

Thank you so much for the peace of mind which you gave us. You will never know how much it aided us.

1. This is one of the signs of over-breathing.

His account of what happened.

David was anxious beforehand it case he should not 'be able to stomach it'. In the event, he rather surprised himself, and this sense of astonishment creeps into his labour report.

During a meal Katrina kept getting contractions lasting about one and a half minutes at two to three minute intervals. She kept asking 'How long was that one?' and 'How long since the previous one?' I thought she was just rehearsing for the real thing, so I was a little impatient with her and told her to stop messing about. It turned out to be the real thing, because just after our meal she called out for me and I rushed upstairs to her. She was in the toilet where she had had a show. She said I had better phone the midwife. I must confess that at this moment I felt a little apprehensive, perhaps scared even, as to whether I should be able to stay with Katrina the whole time, as we had planned, or whether I should be terrified, but this feeling quickly passed as there was much to do, and from then on I was calm. I think it was probably due to the suddenness of it, as there had been no contractions at intervals of an hour or so to give us any warning. I recall that on a few previous days, during our labour rehearsals, she had experienced very strong Braxton-Hicks contractions at intervals of five minutes or less, and lasting up to two minutes: perhaps these were in reality signs of the approaching birth.

The previous evening we had climbed all the stairs at

Covent Garden to the amphitheatre (*Norma* with Joan Sutherland).

Katrina went to bed and the midwife found she was five centimetres dilated at 11.00 p.m. The midwife was accompanied by a pupil midwife, and the three of us calmly drank coffee and ate biscuits while Katrina seemed to be managing on her own with no difficulty, using the breathing techniques she had learnt and practised. In between contractions she was laughing and joking.

At 12.30 a.m. the midwife examined her and found she was three-quarters dilated. The transition stage did not last very long. The midwife reminded her of the transition breathing. Once she told Katrina not to push. She said she wasn't, but the midwife said she was lifting her buttocks off the bed, so must have had the urge to push.

At 1.05 a.m. the midwife examined – found her fully dilated – and broke the membranes. The waters burst, and caused no distress to Katrina. The midwife surprised us by saying, 'You can push now', as it had all happened so quickly.

A couple of times Katrina seemed to find it too much, but a gentle reminder and encouragement from the midwife and all was well for the next contraction. On these two occasions I was a little worried in case Katrina couldn't manage on her own and would be given pethidine, as we wanted to have quite an unaided birth, unless there was any medical reason for the use of drugs. The pupil midwife and I sat on either side of her, supporting her back during each effort. The midwife counted up to ten. Katrina found this rather hard work, and after each one the pupil midwife and I lowered her legs, and then raised them for the next one. I tried to encourage her as I saw the head appearing by saying, 'Not long now'. The second stage lasted half an hour, the baby being born at 1.35 a.m. A mirror was held so that Katrina could see the baby being born. He cried as soon as his head was out, and the rest of him followed very quickly. The placenta followed five minutes later, and I calmly looked at it. I found the

158

actual birth to be a very matter-of-fact process. Throughout, Katrina was very relaxed, and joking between contractions at each stage, apart from the two occasions when I felt she might go to pieces, but didn't, and I am very proud of her. She is a much more relaxed person since the birth of our son, and the help and encouragement from the classes has been invaluable.

A RUSHED LABOUR IN THE WRONG PLACE

Many women having their first babies worry that labour may start when they are away from home or not near the hospital where they planned to have the birth and that then everything will take place so rapidly that they will be caught completely unaware and will panic. This very rarely happens, especially the first time round, but here is an account in which a woman having her first baby had a labour lasting only two hours when she was visiting a friend in Brighton. Compare this with the other rapid birth described on page 52, two very different people having similar kinds of labour.

BABY   7 hours old now.
PLACE OF BIRTH   A home in Brighton, by mistake.
Contractions started suddenly at 3 a.m. after slight rupture of membranes. Staying in Brighton overnight with a good friend, but Max in London – panic. Only needed two pains to convince me that 'this was it'. Got Roger (friend) to phone Max to tell him to come immediately. Thought of having light meal – Roger made cornflakes and hot drinking chocolate. Never got a chance to touch either. *Very very* glad that I'd brought sponge – sucked it, sponged my own face. No space between contractions ever really ...

Down on hands and knees on towel in front of fire – like someone praying to Mecca. Great urge to push, afraid of tearing cervix. But bottom in air and baby's head downwards so not direct pressure on cervix. Push away like an animal – *lots* of noise. *Calm* in between contractions. After twenty to twenty-five minutes, stretching, pushing feeling immense. Call ambulance men. They arrive. They call midwife at local hospital. Offer me Entonox meanwhile. Firmly refused.

Make great helpful noises during pushing, know exactly what I want in between pains, but a bit dazed by the speed of it all. Midwife arrives. Wants me on my back. Instant aggro unfortunately. Very efficient. Me equally bolshi. Tell everyone to fuck off when they say, 'Why not call us before?' – How the hell can you know with your first baby? I push and push –my body does it all for me. I listen to my body. It tells me what to do. Feel very fierce and strong and fighting mad with midwife distracting me, but know I need her. Frightened at opening up to such an extent. She cuts me. No local. Hardly feel it, but feel faintly annoyed. Baby out. 'Put her on my tummy.' She refuses. Baby is fine I can see. I say it again. Midwife gives in: 'Natural Childbirth!' Later I find out she's annoyed because she thinks I'm local resident 'tricking' her into doing home delivery. Max arrives for third stage only, alas. Taken to hospital in ambulance for stitching. Max and Roger came too. Max stays with me through stitching and cleaning up procedure. Baby taken to hot nursery. Great support throughout labour from Roger and his two flatmates (girls) but I antagonised midwife and ambulance men too by my aggressiveness and rudeness!

So glad baby is fine. So desperate because they are warming her up and won't let me hold her. I wait two and a half hours for her. Battle with ward sister too who wants to bathe her before I've touched and smelt her properly. I win! Baby arrives at last. Breastfeed immediately. Lovely hungry baby. Sister even more annoyed. Can't bathe her now she's just fed! Oh dear. So sad because Max wasn't there for any of the labour. Cry and cry. 'Please forgive me for being away from you.' Feel he won't love the baby because he didn't see birth.

Max loving, kind, reassures, but sad too, at missing it all. Max and Roger sent away by Sister at 8 a.m. May come again at 4 p.m. Long time!

Baby beautiful. Feel joyous, weepy, tense, tired, hungry, thirsty, all morning. Re-live labour in my mind. Hope baby will wake to want another feed. Look forward to visiting time.

Thank you for classes. Breathing a great help until second stage. Up and about, pacing up and down for *all* of first stage. Felt natural to be on all fours for second. Home delivery okay but pity midwife didn't enjoy it.

I like the rooming in system. I happen to be in a room of my own. Breast and bottle feeding is meant to be four-hourly, but no one interferes with my protracted demand feeding or tries to force in Cow & Gate. The staff are kind after my preliminary brush with Sister. I have tried to be better mannered since!

I don't like the system of bathing the babies only one hour after birth and the mealtimes and visiting doesn't happen quickly enough today. 4 p.m. seems ages at the moment and I am still incredibly hungry and thirsty despite drinking three jugs of water. No other grumbles at all.

Good social worker – will bring clothes for baby to travel back to London. Seen by the S.H.O., the physio, the paed. etc.

Main feelings at the moment (ten hours afterwards)

(1) Marvellous to have baby there continuously.

(2) Very sorry that Max couldn't share.

(3) Couldn't have coped without N.C.T. instruction and pleased to have my own midwifery knowledge.

Homoeopathic Remedies: Hypercal ointment for nipples. Calendula Tincture in warm water for sponging my very sore perineum.

Arnica 6 in granule form for internal bruising.

Caulophyllum 30 taken three times a day on a Sunday only (i.e. once a week for the last four weeks of pregnancy. This remedy is meant to make labour easy, ripening the cervix. I got many painless Braxton-Hicks contractions from thirty-six weeks onwards after taking it.

Labour was astoundingly quick and easy – marred by me being in the wrong place and an unripe midwife! I would take it for my next baby, but later on in pregnancy – thirty-seven to thirty-eight weeks and prepare carefully for an organised home delivery.

AN ANXIOUS EXPECTANT MOTHER

This account is one of the many in which the woman, 'terrified at the prospect of birth' and with 'mixed emotions' about having the baby, was given emotional support and loving help by understanding members of hospital staff who she felt were 'genuine in their concern and warmth', as well as by her husband, and had a labour and delivery which she says was 'one of the most beautiful' experiences she had ever had. She wrote afterwards that the midwives 'made me feel like the only mother giving birth that day . . . They worked with me, sweated with me and rejoiced with me. I almost felt that it was partly their baby too.' After the baby was born her husband was able to stay with her throughout the day and 'nurses, sisters and doctors were there if you needed them, but no one interfered in your special, newly-formed relationship' with the baby.

I had hoped that my first longed-for baby would not start to arrive in the middle of the night – so convinced was I about not being able to arouse my sleepy-headed husband from his usual deep slumber.

He had snored obliviously through the endless weeks when nature had dragged me to the bathroom, six, seven and sometimes eight times a night and even during the last drawn-out lap when contractions had me up during the small hours working through the N.C.T. breathing routine.

'One morning, you'll wake up and the baby will have arrived without your knowledge,' I joked.

Imagine my surprise when I was violently shaken out of my sleep before dawn on that midsummer's morning to find he had already switched the light on and was sitting bolt upright in bed!

We knew immediately these were not Braxton-Hicks contractions. I managed a weak smile, recalling how one of the first-time mums at our regular Wednesday class had asked: 'How will I know when something is going to happen? I'm so afraid I won't be able to tell the difference.' 'You'll know,' said a second-timer confidently. 'You'll know . . .'

The practice ones were merely pin pricks compared with these monsters, which kicked straight through to my back and up my spine. My legs ached, my whole body shook and I was overcome with nausea. Level A, B, C and even a portion of level D went into force and panic overtook me when I realised none was having any effect. I then broke all previous resolve by bursting into tears. 'If this is just the start, I'm never going to cope,' I wailed. 'I can't go through with it.'

'Yes, you will,' comforted my ever calm husband. 'Come on, I'll breathe with you – remember how we practised, himmmmm, aaaaahhhhh, himmmmmmmmm, aaaaahhhhh. That's better, you're calmer now, try to get some sleep.'

But sleep had still eluded me two hours later at 6 a.m. though I was now more confident in the power of the breathing. 'Please don't let it be a false alarm,' I pleaded as David dialled the magical number and asked for the sister on the labour ward. 'Let me see my little baby today.'

David's mum, by chance staying with us for a few days, leapt out of bed at the sign of activity. But it was to be a long and tedious wait.

'Don't come in until the pains are five minutes apart and regular,' was the hospital's advice.

They were as painful as a prize-fighter's punch by now, but still fifteen to twenty minutes apart.

I decided keeping active would be the best distraction – it's always worked with crippling period pains – wash my hair, have a bath, prepare my casserole, work on my scrapbook. But the pains knocked me right off my feet and I was confined to the settee.

The fear was replaced by concentration on the intense breathing, which miraculously fulfilled its intention, and the excitement that the longer the contractions persisted, the sooner it would all be over.

David and his mum continually complimented me on the way I handled the pains. Certainly I wasn't shedding any more tears or experiencing the same panic I had had on awaking. Not until the ambulance pulled up at 2.05 p.m., that is.

Never having been in hospital before, I was terrified at the thought of what the rest of the day held in store. I stifled the tears as, clutching my tiny case, I kissed David's mum and realised that the next time she saw me my whole body and whole being would have been overtaken by a dramatic and miraculous change.

Contractions were coming fiercely now and the journey took longer than usual because of heavy traffic. The sun burned through the window, making me feel sick. The vehicle was claustrophobic and I wanted to jump out into the fresh air. But finally we swerved onto the hospital forecourt and within seconds a wheelchair was at my feet and as I was whisked away, the friendly ambulanceman shouted: 'Good luck, hope you get what you want.'

I had wanted David by my side every inch of the way, but we were parted on leaving the lift for about three hours. The nurses almost made up for his absence though. Gently they explained all that was happening and prepared for the first two things I was dreading – the shave and enema.

Contractions were coming so fast, I lost count, but not, it seems, control.

'See you've been doing your exercises,' one of the nurses said. 'Good girl, that's why you're so relaxed.'

Finally stripped of my clothes and clad in the unflattering gown, I was led down to the delivery room, a kindly sister hugging me through the difficult pains.

For the umpteenth time, I was asked about painkillers – epidural, pethidine, gas and air. I wanted none of them, convinced I could manage on the N.C.T. training alone. But after an internal examination, sister insisted I have a dose of pethidine. 'Baby's posterior position, that's why it's so painful,' she said. 'We usually advise people to have an epidural in these cases.'

That was definitely out and by the time she administered the injection, without asking my permission again, I was too engrossed in discomfort to resist.

At some point I remember seeing a familiar, smiling face appear at my side in cap and gown. Was it after they had broken my waters and clumsily fitted the glucose drip – the nervous student had to have four attempts at finding a vein? But David's tender, concerned face was certainly a welcome sight.

I didn't have much to say to him, no friendly chats or games of Scrabble as we had planned: I was too busy concentrating on controlling the pain. At 6 p.m. the sister examined me again and shrieked everyone into action when she said: 'My goodness, this girl's well into labour,' and to me exclaimed: 'You were so relaxed I thought nothing was happening.'

But this was the time when I thought I lost all control. I was told to turn onto my side, the large dose of pethidine by now taking its full effect and then something horrific started to happen. I had a violent and uncontrollable urge to push. Remembering the N.C.T. advice, I tried huff-huff puff-puffing, encouraged by David. But to no effect. I was desperate, the bearing down I had read so much about was happening and I couldn't stop it. In my only emotional outburst, I grabbed the student and pleaded with him to let me push. He coolly refused.

Blissfully, Sister appeared minutes later and told me I could. And hard, perspiring, frustrating work though it was, it seemed considerably less painful than the ordinary labour pains. Perhaps because at last, I knew I was getting somewhere. At 4.30 p.m. the Sister had said she hoped the baby would be born before she went off duty at 9 p.m. and I was horrified to think I might have to wait that long. But here we were at 7 p.m., the time seemingly having spun by.

'Work with me, and we'll have it here by half past,' she said soothingly. I nodded. But push as I might and encouraged by an ecstatic David who could see the top of the baby's hairy head, virtually nothing happened for an hour. Amazingly I didn't scream or rant as I feared I might. I so desperately wanted to prove to myself and everyone else that I could do it with the minimum fuss. I kept up with the breathing routine, though surprisingly didn't venture into my well rehearsed song, 'Baby Face'.

But when at 7.45 p.m. all seemed at a standstill and I was virtually unaware of what was going on, the doctor called in to say that if the baby hadn't arrived by eight he would 'do something about it'. That shook me out of my drowsiness.

Five minutes to go to the doctor's deadline and still stalemate. Two minutes and a desperate plea from Sister : 'Push, Vanessa, please, please make it a good one for me, just for me.'

I nodded and with the next contraction, I hugged up my knees, took three short breaths, one deep one and pushed, pushed with all my might.

The sudden sharp stab was frightening. I screamed, but David doesn't remember me doing so and something shot out like a rocket. It was slithery and soft and I remember seeing my tummy go down like a deflated balloon. What's happening to me, I thought, what was that?

Only when I heard David's emotion-packed voice say: 'Oh it's a little boy,' did I realise it was all over. 'A little boy, my baby, after all these years, all the months of discomfort, no more worrying, fear, it's over. Let me see him, is he all right? Can I hold him? David you're crying. Oh isn't it lovely?' This jumble of sentences tripped out of my head.

The sisters, nurses and students were dancing jubilantly when, just as promised, the doctor appeared at the door asking: 'How's she doing?' 'Go away, she's done it on her own,' they chorused.

Little Simon, a screaming little scrap of redness with a mass of sticky brown hair was placed in his perspex crib.

'That little being has been inside me for nine months,' I mused. 'Now he's part of the world, our world.' There were no tears of emotion from me, the normally soppy sentimentalist. With David's arm around me, I burst into a fit of giggles, pain and discomfort seeming a million miles away.

'Is he all right?' I yelled to the jolly coloured nurse who broke off her singing and said: 'Course he is, just listen to him. Would you like to hold him?'

Silly question. A moment of a lifetime. Little Simon ten minutes old, blood-stained, with twisted mouth and one eye closed, was placed into my arms. 'I'm a mother. This is my baby,' I thought. As long as I live, I shall always feel the powerful heat generating from his tiny body at that moment. I expected to recognise him, but all I could see was an ugly, distorted little face. 'Isn't he funny looking?' I exclaimed and David, who had always declared that all babies had peculiar faces exclaimed: 'No, he's beautiful.'

'Ready to be stitched up,' said a familiar voice – which gave David the cue to ring the new grandmothers.

It was a long and tricky process and the doctor apologised for keeping me 'hanging around' for half an hour.

'Don't worry,' I beamed, still high with elation. 'Chop my leg off now for all I care.'

Three hours later, back in the ward with all the other mums, I trembled with joy at all that had been fulfilled. No longer just an ordinary woman, I had achieved that girlhood dream of motherhood. My love for David and his for me had created a new being. He was perfect, no damage, no irregularities. And I was all right. I'd done it without too much bother. Oh wonderful night. But where was this long sleep I had been promised? It wouldn't come and in the morning at 6 o'clock when a cheerful voice appeared at my bedside saying: 'Mrs B., here's your little boy,' I was out of bed in a flash.

I had a lot of learning to do and lots to tell my little son.

The other mothers commented on my activity and exuberance. For the first time in nine months, I felt at the peak of health and happiness.

The Father's Account

David wrote this the night he arrived home after sharing in what he called 'the most thrilling event' of his life.

The night before I'd had to drive up to Birmingham for my work, and I didn't return home until two in the morning.

Previously when Vanessa had experienced minor contractions at night I'd hardly noticed, being a heavy and sound sleeper. But for some reason when, at four in the morning, I suddenly realised that she was going through her breathing exercises again, something made me understand that this was different.

We'd read accounts of labour where the parents-to-be were able to go out for a stroll or play piano duets, but this wasn't possible for Vanessa! We timed the contractions and I tried to keep her controlled and in command of her breathing and soon after 6 a.m. I rang the hospital to ask their advice.

Don't come in until the contractions are coming at regular five-minute intervals, we were told.

Vanessa had to concentrate hard all morning to keep in command of her breathing and did very well, it seemed to me. It was clearly extremely painful and uncomfortable and during the morning it was all she could do to have a little breakfast and a bath.

All along we'd been afraid of being disappointed by a false alarm, so I think that helped keep us calm early on because we didn't want to build up our hopes that this would be the day until it was absolutely certain.

Once or twice the contractions spaced out, but after one o'clock at lunchtime they had speeded up and were approaching the five-minute mark.

Finally it was time to phone the hospital, warn the ward, and call the ambulance.

When it arrived Vanessa held up matters by having a contraction halfway down the front path, and then the ambulance – trying to find a short cut back to the main road – got lost in the side-streets. Finally, while the driver sorted himself out his colleague timed Vanessa's contractions and very soon we were driving into the hospital courtyard.

There was a wheelchair to meet us and the ambulance men wished us good luck and – 'Hope you get what you want.'

At that stage it didn't seem to matter much whether the baby was boy or girl – the main concern at the back of our minds was just that it would be healthy.

Vanessa was wheeled round the corridors and into the lift and I followed along with her case, a bit like a porter at a loose end. Then, while Vanessa was being prepared I was shown into the fathers' room. I'd taken some papers I needed to go through and a couple of apples and in the midst of my reading I looked up just in time to see Vanessa being led along the corridor.

After that I went back to my reading. It seemed ages I was waiting, and I'd long finished my work before they finally told me I could don cap and gown and join Vanessa. This was about 4.30, two and a half hours after we'd arrived.

I wondered what had taken so long – I'd been afraid I might miss something, or that they'd forget I was there!

In fact there was still plenty of time. Vanessa had been given a heavy dose of pethidine to help her relax and enable her to get some rest between contractions. She wasn't too sure of my presence, so I wiped her face with iced water from time to time and at one stage she came out of her haze just long enough to say: 'I never want to go through this again – ever.'

Needless to say it wasn't long after – a matter of days – that she was changing her mind!

Every so often a sister or nurse would come in to see how

170

the baby was progressing and I was shooed back to the waiting room. Finally, at long last, it was time to start pushing.

The midwife had congratulated Vanessa on being so relaxed through her breathing, but now the hard work was about to start! It wasn't very long – or it didn't seem so to me – that we could see the top of the baby's head and a little wet crop of straggly hair.

Since he was facing the wrong way the business was complicated a little, and probably took longer than might have been the case had he been facing upwards. As I saw the top of the little head I wondered: 'Is it a boy, or girl?'

At that stage, preparatory for delivery, I was moved round to the other side of the bed.

'There's a stool by the bed there, you can sit down if you like,' said the midwife. She had obviously had her work complicated by previous expectant fathers crumpling into a heap at the vital stage, but I was too excited to want to sit down.

I thought to myself: I'm going to remember every moment of this. I felt as if history was being made! Of course, it was easy for me – I didn't have any of the pain or hard work or exhausting effort.

The delivery seemed to happen very quickly. The senior doctor had wandered in, concerned that a forceps delivery might be necessary but while he was out of the room first a little head emerged, then suddenly the baby's body came shooting out, as if it were jet-propelled and it couldn't wait to get into the world.

I just had time for a quick glance to tell Vanessa, 'It's a boy!'

He didn't appear as mucky or messy as I expected. In fact, the whole birth was much less gory than I'd expected from reading the books and watching the films. The arrival of our first baby, a son, into the world, took away all fear I'd had of nausea at the machinery of birth.

I was shooed out now while Vanessa was cleaned up, and took the opportunity to phone both mothers. Then I was able to go back and be with my wife and son.

Vanessa had now started to come round from the effects of the drug and could cradle the baby in her arms.

'You hold him,' she said, but I didn't want to. I'd had no experience of babies before, and he seemed so small and fragile I was afraid I'd drop him or crush him.

So, instead, he was laid back into his hospital cot where he remained, gently blowing bubbles at us.

YIN AND YAN

The mother writes:

It was very much a joint effort. Without John I'm afraid I never would have made it. He played the most important part, and felt with me in a joint experience of the most important event in our lives. The tangible creation of our love was actually born, as well as conceived, in love. She is a very lucky baby, and so are we.

10.30 p.m. Castor oil, gin, Ribena taken.(1)

1.10 a.m. Sleep.

4.00 a.m. Contractions commencing, two minutes apart. nurse.

4.30 a.m. Nurse arrived. Contractions still two minutes apart, length one minute.
My husband breathed with me. I told husband I had to have bowel movement. (Of course it was merely the baby's head.)

5.00 a.m. Membranes were ruptured by nurse. Cervix was not fully dilated. Urge to bear down, but not unbearable – I merely panted. Impulse lasted length of contraction. Very hard to concentrate.

5.20–5.25 a.m. Birth time. Bearing down impulse not really very violent. Only once at beginning did I truly feel the urge to bear down, and then it was weak. Nurse told me to bear down. Husband held me, encouraged me. Desire to hold him, grasp him – didn't want him to leave me, even long enough to sponge my dry mouth. The head crowned. Then two or three more pushes and baby's head was born. Nurse clamped the cord. She said – 'Now push only a little on the next contraction.' I did, and all the water rushed out over baby. Then one more push and her body came out. Very little mucus. She did not want to cry – only yelped once. Placenta was removed from me by nurse gently kneading abdomen. One stitch needed.

Note

1. The doctor had advised starting labour off, as the expected date of delivery was well past. The gin and Ribena simply cut the greasiness of the oil, which is the active principle. This method of inducing labour – part of an 'O.B.E.' – (oil, bath, enema) is only useful if the woman is really ripe for labour. It is often only effective between 12 and 24 hours after.

The father writes:

I was awakened at approximately 3.00 a.m. by my wife in the bathroom. She told me she felt labour was beginning. I propped her up in bed. It took us all of half an hour to establish reasonable harmony of breathing with contractions. I breathed with her through all levels. I insisted that she breathe properly and relax; otherwise it would hurt. I did not remain a logical adviser, but rather a catalyst, acting through the spontaneity of love rather than logical detachment. I have the glorious realisation that I have emotional harmony with my wife.

We established harmony with the breathing, after which I left to call the midwife. I had Pippa on her side, she found this more comfortable, and was rubbing her back and breathing simultaneously with her when the midwife arrived. I was by this time wholly involved in the labour, and her breath was my breath. This was undistilled love, a oneness some only achieve through copulation.

The midwife determined that the front part of the cervix was all that barred my baby's descent. She instructed my wife not to bear down but to continue to breathe with the contractions. We both continued, and when we blew out at the end of a contraction I gave her a puff from my joint.

Now came the bearing down stage and the most painfully beautiful experience I have ever had. My wife was in a sitting position now. I had my right arm around her back with my hand under her arm supporting her, while her left arm was around my neck.

I knew there was no point in my saying, 'Relax honey', I had to feel it with her. The perspiration was running down my back. I said, 'Come on honey, deep breath – now bear down!! Hold on, hold on!! Now breathe.'

I could see a tiny portion of the baby's head lightly covered with black hair. The nurse made a small incision in the perineum. My wife and I took a breath and bore down. 'Bear down honey, it's coming! Bear down, bear down, hold on, hold on.' The baby's head popped out fully exposed to the neck. Along with it came the umbilical cord and nurse clamped it. My wife was told to pant and push gently on the next one.

The perspiration was rolling off my head. Then the glorious moment when the little being was wholly released from the vagina. The nurses turned the baby round. 'It's a girl, honey!' I shouted, 'It's a girl, honey!' I was beside myself with joy. I had given birth along with my wife. I was exhausted. It was glorious, just glorious.

Whoever said that a joint endeavour of husband and wife in natural childbirth was extremely fulfilling did not come anywhere near describing the ecstasy I experienced. We are so very happy. This experience has made a bond between us that no ordinary birth, nor in fact any other experience, could have done. We have a sense of rapport that goes far beyond anything I have ever experienced or observed. Emotional harmony, physical harmony, mental harmony. We have all three. Turbulent and passionate as it is – Yin and Yan – we are so blessed.

A CAESAREAN SECTION

My baby was born by Caesarean section. There had always been this possibility because of an ovarian cyst. I went into hospital on the expected day and after five days' wait and no contractions at all, they suddenly decided to operate. I was eating my tea at 3.00 p.m. on Monday when I was told they would do it at 7.30 that evening, so I was denied a second piece of cake.

My husband was allowed to be present, and I had an epidural, so could hear all and feel some. They put a screen over my tummy, so I couldn't see my own inside, but John stood behind me holding my hand, and he had a full view.(1) The theatre seemed full of doctors, nurses and students, all anxious to watch.

Mr W. did the operation (very neatly). When the baby had been lifted out and past my line of vision they found the cyst and cut that off the ovary.

The baby weighed 9 lb 7 oz and is really beautiful. She has fair skin and hair and is very long. We call her Lucinda. She has been good and is progressing nicely.

Note

1. This is only done with specially prepared parents, and usually at their request.

AN 'ELDERLY PRIMIP' OF 38

10.00 a.m. approximately, labour began. Mild contractions throughout morning which did not interfere with normal activities.

1.00 p.m. Light lunch (a mistake this!).

1.30 p.m. One-minute contractions every ten minutes – beginning to be uncomfortable and I had to sit down during a contraction.

2.00 p.m. Left for hospital – three contractions on thirty-minute journey – I started controlled breathing.

2.35 p.m. Enema, bath and preparation. My husband was sent out for tea after seeing me settled in bed.

5.00 p.m. Two-minute contractions every three minutes, continuing with increasing strength until . . .

6.50 p.m. Pethidine injection was given. Two fingers dilated.

7.00 p.m. Vomited. Felt sick thereafter. My husband was sent out for supper.

8.20 p.m. The membranes were broken by the doctor.

9.15 p.m. Second pethidine injection. For four hours contractions had seemed almost continuous, although as far as I remember I did the breathing automatically, as I had practised. I was aware all the time of being relaxed. In fact I remember feeling that it was infinitely *easier* to let myself go completely. I don't think I was fighting the contractions.

9.50 p.m. To delivery room – second stage just started.

The baby was born at 10.28 p.m., so we were in the delivery room forty minutes. Looking back on this period it seems like a dream, but I was apparently talking coherently, and must have been more composed than I now think. I found this stage exhilarating. I watched the baby's head crowning, then did the appropriate breathing and blowing so that the rest of the birth was held up while the cord was cut; this was round the baby's neck and had to be pulled out and clamped and cut – all of which I watched while the Sister directed my breathing. The rest of Kate shot out like a sardine. I was injected with ergometrine at the moment of her total exit, and the placenta followed almost immediately.

By now I felt suddenly and completely clear headed. I asked the Sister if we could see the placenta, and she gave us a most interesting little lecture on it, all of which I took in and remembered. Then we drank cups of tea, and I ate cornflakes.

ANOTHER FORCEPS DELIVERY

This mother felt very uncertain about her ability to relax, especially the muscles of the pelvic floor. Her baby was posterior.

I went into hospital to be induced the following day. However that night at 1.15 a.m. the waters broke so the induction was unnecessary. The contractions began a couple of hours later.

By 5.00 a.m. the contractions were coming at five-minute intervals and I was taken up to the labour ward. I was then able to ask for Pete who arrived about half an hour later. Meanwhile I was told that, as I was in the very early stages and had no sleep that night I ought to have an injection of pethidine, which would help me sleep until labour really was under way. The contractions became more severe and I felt drowsy in between. Pete was a real comfort and was able to rub my back for me, which made things much easier. The breathing was very useful.

I began bearing down at about 11.00 a.m. when the head was just visible. I worked as hard as I was able. An hour later only a very small part of the head could be seen. Another doctor was sent for and I was told that forceps would have to be used to deliver the baby. There was some discussion on the heartbeats of the baby. They prepared me for a forceps delivery. I was still aware of what was going on, and I remember how thrilled I was that Pete was allowed to stay during the forceps delivery.

They turned the baby inside me and then at 12.50 p.m. pulled him out with forceps. I was completely conscious and I was so overjoyed when he cried immediately and Pete and I both said, 'It's a boy!' I remained very wide-awake and very happy while they stitched me up and the doctor explained the whole process to Pete and me as he did it. The baby is very healthy. He weighed 7 lb 15 oz when born and had already put on 12 oz when the midwife weighed him at ten days old. I came home from hospital three days after he was born as Pete was able to be home with me. I'm very pleased to be able to feed him myself, and he's good at feeding, although he gets rather overwhelmed when the milk comes fast at first.

Thank you for showing me what I'm sure is the right approach to childbirth.

A LONG LABOUR

I had a baby girl yesterday morning. She was born easily and naturally after a twenty-three and a half hour labour.

Fortunately when labour started the head was in line with the brim of the cervix, though much too high, although it had been slightly crooked the previous day. It took the first fifteen hours to push the head down. With the help of your exercises I found this time not even particularly tiring, and certainly not unpleasant. Then the contractions began to intensify, though still coming at seven-minute intervals. At 10.30 p.m. I had an injection to help me sleep, as I was told I needed some rest and the baby would not be born that night. My husband went home to get some sleep.

At 1 o'clock I woke up with strong, frequent contractions and was sent up to the labour ward. There I was left in my own bed in the x-ray room. I was very dopey, but was still able to control the contractions. My husband arrived at 2.00 a.m. (He was told I'd be a very long time before giving birth.) There seemed to be no respite between contractions. I was also sick. Soon after that my husband called a nurse and our daughter was born in an ordinary bed wedged up against the x-ray bed, so that no one could get at me properly. She weighed 7 lb 13 oz and I had no stitches.

Until the last half hour I was completely relaxed, yet exhilarated. My whole attitude to childbearing is quite different now. In fact I almost want to have another baby merely to prove I can do it twice! The doctor looking after me was quite astonished that it had all been so easy. She had left instructions that she was to be called when things started happening, but of course no one had time to telephone her.

I CAN'T DESCRIBE THE JOY I FELT

Labour began very mildly at 9.00 p.m. with contractions at seven-minute intervals. By 11.00 p.m. they were still the same, and there had been no show or breaking of waters, so we decided to go to bed. By 1.30 a.m. I was still awake and the contractions were very close; timing found them to be at one-and-a-half-minute intervals and lasting half a minute.

The midwife, Nurse B., arrived about 2.15 a.m. and, after examining me, said the baby would probably arrive just in time for breakfast. I was five centimetres dilated. She was very pleased to find that I was one of your pupils, and was most helpful with keeping me informed of my progress and keeping clear my view of the mirror that my husband set up at the end of the bed.

I managed the first stage well. My husband was by my side throughout my labour, massaging my back and being generally encouraging. When the contractions became really strong it seemed to me that they started right on their peak and I was never able to prepare for them, particularly at the end of the first stage when they were very close together. The midwife broke the waters herself. With her and my husband to encourage me I was determined to stay on top of the contractions. Afterwards the midwife told me that she thought I would have to ask for the gas and air towards the end. Fortunately she didn't offer it or try in any way to influence me.

I had to fight sleep in the second stage. I would have given anything to shut my eyes and leave everything to those around me, but neither the midwife nor the contractions would allow me to do so. The mirror was very successful. I was able to see the baby's head move backwards and forwards and began to feel really excited about seeing the whole of her soon.

I had earlier asked the midwife to tell me if I wasn't to push. When the head was ready to emerge she asked me not to push for a few contractions. I started panting, but after only a few seconds I just had to push. This happened with subsequent contractions, and our daughter, Isobel, burst forth into the world at 5.10 a.m., two hours sooner than the midwife had calculated from her earlier examination. I can't describe the joy I felt as I held her close and listened to her loud complaints.

I am very grateful for having been taught how to actively take part in my baby's birth, and not just lie there and let it happen to me. It's an experience I will always cherish.

To those mothers who can't quite decide whether or not to have their husbands present I say, 'Please do!' I couldn't have managed without the moral support and encouragement that mine gave me.

A MOTHER WHO WASN'T QUITE SURE SHE WANTED TO BE ONE

You will be pleased to hear that we now have a baby daughter born on August bank holiday Monday. The birth was a wonderful experience, and we are both very thrilled with the baby.

I had a very short labour with very little warning that it was about to commence. We went out on Sunday evening, and I had no idea that it was the beginning of labour. At 10.00 p.m. strong contractions suddenly began, coming at four-minute intervals and lasting approximately one minute. At 11.00 p.m. I had a show and we rang the midwife. She arrived at midnight, by which time the contractions were coming on top of each other. I was able to manage the breathing. At 1.45 a.m. I got on the bed as I felt a slight urge to bear down. The nurse's examination revealed that I was four fingers dilated. By 2.15 a.m. I was fully dilated.

As I was feeling very hot, the cold sponge was marvellous and I would not be parted from it until the baby was born. Contractions were now less frequent, but I found the next hour to be the most difficult. I felt tired. I couldn't believe it when the nurse said the head was visible. At this point the waters broke and I was greatly relieved.

My husband reminded me constantly to keep my chin down. I couldn't stand being touched,(1) and so he wasn't able to hold me up or massage my tummy. When the head crowned I suddenly felt in control again and was able to breathe my baby out. It was a wonderful feeling. I felt very wide awake after the birth and was pleased to be able to help the midwife find everything that was needed. She was Mrs B. and her presence made me feel happier right from the

184

start. She was very kind, helping my husband with the back rubbing, and when she realised I was getting muddled in the bearing-down process she became quite firm, which is just what I needed.

As to whether I love my baby, which was my chief pregnancy fear, her dear little face is never far from my thoughts, although her reality is still hard to grasp at times.

I am still bombarded from all sides by people who tell me not to do this and that, as I was in my pregnancy. I am gradually learning not to get upset by this and just humour them. My husband has been marvellous throughout, being wonderful at the birth, and then looking after me so well. I'm sure it would have been all a terrifying experience had I not attended the classes. We are so grateful!

Note
1. This is a fairly common experience in advanced labour.

THE WARM, SLIPPERY FEELING AS I LIFTED MY BABY TOWARDS ME...

In this account a single mother describes the emotional support and loving help she received from her antenatal teacher and a woman friend who were both with her during labour. The baby was born with a heart condition (later surgically corrected) and in retrospect she was extremely glad that she was able to labour without pain-relieving drugs which might have been dangerous for her especially vulnerable little daughter.

When my enthusiastic news of the pregnancy failed to evoke a similar response from the father, but instead resulted in the total deterioration of our relationship, I was left with a difficult decision: abortion or the label, lifelong, perhaps, of unmarried mother. After the necessary soul-searching, I plumped for the latter, and more fortunate than most, no doubt, in this I had the loving support of family and friends.

I had been studying for advanced qualifications. When I realised that I was pregnant, I started the task of cramming a year's work into only eight months. The success of my financial future would depend on these efforts.

I arranged with Louise, one of my closest friends, to be with me during delivery. Together we were to attend Pauline's N.C.T. classes. I also began using a self-hypnosis technique, part of the psychotherapy course I was taking. The suggestions which I gave myself were 'to remain calm, relaxed, controlled and free from fear'. I did not include the suggestion that the experience would be painless, only that pain should not so overwhelm me as to prevent me from functioning consciously and naturally. Throughout my preg-

186

nancy I used the same technique to grow more in tune with my body and closer to my baby.

At five months I began attending classes. Louise came with me on the nights normally open to husbands. It was great to have her there, but nevertheless, inside, I felt rather lonely, out of place and conspicuous on those nights.

Louise and I were not always able to get together for discussion and practice of the exercises. However, as my time drew nearer, Pauline was approached to see if she would attend the delivery. Happily, this she was glad to do, and I felt much comforted to know that her experience and wonderful personality would no doubt elicit greater co-operation from busy hospital staff, who might not be in entire accord with my determination to give birth to my baby in as natural a manner as possible.

A good two weeks before the baby was due I was getting twinges, Braxton-Hicks contractions and backache. A crisis occurred at this time: my father was rushed to hospital for emergency surgery. Things became frenzied as, between visiting hours, I found myself dashing into town constantly to buy last-minute things such as freezellas, sponges, glucose tablets – all part of my labour kit! I even bought smelling salts in case anyone fainted!

The staff on my father's ward, as well as the more experienced female members of my family, assured me that I would be having the baby any day. This was not comforting, as it happened, because Pauline was to be on holiday. Now, I can't help wondering how Pauline knew, when she confidently told me over the phone, 'There is no need to worry! You won't have the baby before I get back.'

Meanwhile, during Pauline's absence, there was a hot-line between Louise and myself. One night her phone was not properly replaced; the next morning she phoned me in a highly agitated state. Upon hearing my voice she said, with obvious relief, 'Thank goodness, you haven't had it yet!'

The night before my expected confinement, I put my suitcase by the back door, together with a miniature cognac bottle containing three large daisies; they were for focusing upon during labour. I then set my hair, and before switching off the bedside light I carefully rehearsed my breathing exercises, and mentally reviewed all I had been taught in my classes. The next day I was woken by the baby taking its early morning exercise and didn't have the slightest inclination to give birth.

That same day, my father was allowed to come home, after complaining bitterly that he didn't want to become a grandfather in hospital. His doctor wished me luck, saying that most women could not stand the pain of natural childbirth. He went on to say that he had been present at such a birth on one occasion only, '. . . the woman went through her labour waving her arms about and singing "Old MacDonald Had a Farm". Most disconcerting!'

There was still a week to go before Pauline got back. Anxiety levels were rising. Louise complained of sleep deprivation. My twinges were becoming more regular and I had something which looked very much like a 'show'. At long last Pauline phoned 'I'm back! You can have your baby now.'

From then on, as each day went by, my impatience grew. In order to keep from brooding, I restarted work on a rug which I had begun seven years previously.

On the Thursday evening I began to get definite contractions every twenty minutes, then fifteen, lasting for half a minute. Not strong enough to breathe through but very definitely there. At ten o'clock that night I phoned Pauline. 'Keep timing them and phone back in half an hour.' The contractions were soon coming every ten minutes and I was using level 'A' breathing. Phoned Pauline again. 'You had better come over!'

The plan was for Louise and I to meet at Pauline's home, which is only minutes from the hospital. We would wait there drinking tea and counting contractions until the last possible moment. I dialled Louise's number and a voice on the other end said, 'I'm sorry! She's in bed. Could you phone back tomorrow?' After hurried explanations, Louise, very wide awake, came to the telephone. 'Right. It's action stations. Have you got the flasks and the ice? See you at Pauline's.' My parents bundled me and suitcase into the car and off we went, cognac bottle with the same three daisies, over a week old but still fresh, held firmly in my hand.

I was greeted at Pauline's with much excitement. Louise was there, ready with a hug and a kiss and Pauline's two nightgown-clad little girls were hanging over the banister rail.

Moments later I was sitting in the living room with a cup of tea and *no* contractions! They had disappeared as I came in through the front door. At one o'clock in the morning I phoned Mum to tell her to relax and get a good night's sleep and was amazed to hear her voice before the first ring had finished sounding. She had pitched up the camp bed by the telephone.

Once in bed I tossed and turned, willing my contractions to come back and muttering under my breath, 'Just trust something like this to happen!' Around two o'clock I thought my prayers were being answered. I began to have some contractions. But, wisely, I decided not to sound the alarm until absolutely certain. I shut my eyes and dozed off. At four I awoke with a start; the contractions had gone again. I sat up in bed feeling tired and dejected and then had a little cry. I couldn't sleep. By six the backache, a pain which had been with me for several weeks, had also gone. I went to the loo and had a positive 'show'.

The day was promising to be warm and sunny. After bath and breakfast, Pauline suggested that Louise and I go for a walk. We decided to visit a friend nearby and then do some window shopping in town. During the visit my contractions returned. However, after previous false alarms I was doubly determined to say and do nothing until it became quite obvious.

While we were shopping I began to feel confident that the contractions *were* going to stay. In the glass and china shop, during a particularly strong contraction, I looked around desperately for something to lean on. The shop assistant said, 'Can I help you?' I smiled at her through clenched teeth and realised that I had better get back to the security of Pauline's kitchen and the clock with its large second hand.

Lunchtime back at Pauline's, eating bread and honey and sipping tea between contractions, I began to realise just how important the breathing was going to be in maintaining control. At two in the afternoon the contractions were coming in waves. 2.14 thirty seconds . . . 2.16 fifty seconds . . . 2.19 thirty seconds . . . 2.23 forty-five seconds. Pauline phoned the hospital. 'Bring her in,' they said.

I remember being suddenly aware of lots of little girls; two of them I recognised as Pauline's daughters. They were watching with open interest as I was once again bundled into the car, together with suitcase, daisies and two plastic carrier bags containing my labour kit. In the hospital we were ushered into a tiny waiting room. I became acutely aware of the enormous amount of baggage I had brought, and also that my contractions had stopped again. The freezellas had been forgotten! They were still sitting, at the ready, in a pan of hot water on Pauline's stove. The contractions started up again and off I went for shave and suppositories. Pauline rushed back for the freezellas. Once home, she was greeted by her intrigued offspring with the question, 'Has she had it yet?'

At 3.45 p.m. my waters were broken. I was eight centimetres dilated and did not feel happy about the experience. Shortly afterwards a nurse told me to choose which of my two friends should stay with me during the delivery. I tried, unsuccessfully, to explain that special permission had been given for them *both* to remain. The nurse was adamant. 'You must choose!' I awaited the verdict, fortunate to be in one of the few delivery suites with a window. The sun was streaming in and a cheery midwife entered. 'I've just come in to tell you *both* your friends will be with you soon, they're just getting dressed now.' Then she gave me a hug saying,

'It's simply marvellous,' and bustled out. In the difficult days that were to come this midwife proved a great comfort.

Louise and Pauline entered, looking like sheepish milk-maids. I was helped off the bed into a chair packed with pillows and hot freezella in the small of my back. The contractions were coming strongly and I timed them by the clock on the wall.

At 4.32 the baby's heart beat was measured; it was 150. The electric blanket was put into the cot. My contractions became long and painful. All my concentration was focused on breathing, with a fixed obsessional gaze on the clock. My daisies were forgotten, and I had long ago given up timing.

Louise and Pauline were indispensable. They ministered damp cloths to my brow, sprays of perfumed water, juicy wet sponges to suck, hot packs for my backache and effleurage to my tummy, which was very soothing. Their understanding of my needs was almost telepathic, aided only by an occasional grunt or shake of my head. I had given permission for students to be present and occasionally one would wander in, stay awhile, attempt to converse with me and then leave with what looked like a bad case of boredom. Eventually a young doctor *did* decide to stay. He was concerned that I did not ask for pethidine.

By 5.50 p.m. my contractions were two minutes long and no let up. I was put onto the bed pan and then onto the bed, still in an upright position. Sitting up, I felt in control. But I was not happy about being moved; there was not enough time between contractions and I disliked having my concentration interrupted.

I asked about gas and oxygen. It was suggested by Pauline that I hang on until I found out how far dilated I was. I was told that gas and air would make me feel drunk, and as I was already feeling nauseous, I didn't fancy the idea. Tiredness was overcoming me. I felt shivery, very nauseous and had an uncomfortable feeling as if I were sitting upon a melon. 'This is awful! How much longer?'

Pauline said, 'You're in transition.'

At 5.59 the clock stopped. Louise came to the rescue and I was soon contemplating three white daisies which she had placed at the foot of the bed. She began massaging my feet and I was surprised at how comforting this was.

The clock did start again and by 6.14 I began 'blowing out candles'. Louise and Pauline blew them out with me. As the attending nurse was preparing to go off duty, she patted me on the head saying, 'Don't worry! You are bound to have it by tonight!'

At 7.20 I was rolled from my secure position onto my side. The uterine contractions were very powerful. Trying *not* to push was hard enough, but on my side it was almost impossible. For a brief moment I came very close to losing control. I clung to Louise and cried out, 'Help me'. Even now I am not sure why I was rolled over. I never bothered to find out. I was soon sitting up again, pillows and hot pack in place. Not long after I received the comforting news that the baby would probably be born about 8 p.m. It was just what I needed to hear.

By 8 p.m. the baby had not arrived, but I was told I could begin pushing. It was such a relief! Real team work followed and that was marvellous. I had one arm around Louise and Pauline. A super midwife gave me very precise guidance and I had no difficulty getting into the feel of my body and pushing for all I was worth! I had to be catheterised and then the pushing began again. As the baby's head began to crown I heard Louise's excited voice, 'Black hair! Lots of black hair!' From then on all I remember was pushing and voices. 'Open up', 'It's coming', 'Anybody would think it was her sixth, not her first.'

The midwife asked me if she could bring in some more students and I heard her calling outside the door, 'Hurry!' I do not know how many came in, for by that time I was not interested. All I was thinking about was that black hair, and then I saw my baby's head appear. It started to cry and I fell back against the pillows.

'Have you got names for your baby?' asked the midwife.

'If it is a boy, Daniel Peter. If it is a girl, Zoë, I haven't thought of a middle name.' The midwife seemed pleased that I had been prepared for either sex. 'So many women come in with definite expectations and then they're disappointed.' I didn't bother to tell her that until the week before I had been convinced my baby was a boy and then suddenly found myself hoping for a girl. I was pondering upon this thought as the midwife said, 'When you're ready I want you to give a big push and then, when I tell you, bring your arms down and lift your baby onto your tummy.'

As if her words had been a magic formula a contraction started. I went along with it! The events which followed took on, for me, a slow motion, other-worldly effect! I remember seeing my hands reaching out for my baby and was vaguely aware of Pauline preventing a nurse from covering up my midriff and the nurse's retort, 'But it's messy!' I remember the strange, warm, slippery feeling as I took hold and lifted my baby towards me, in the distance someone said, 'It's a girl!' and I held her against me and said, 'Hello, little Zoë! What a beautiful little thing you are!'

Everything and everyone receded into another time, and for a few precious moments Zoë and I were all that was. Someone said, 'Isn't she alert!' I replied, 'Yes, and Zoë means *Life!*'

At 8.24 Zoë had come into the world weighing 7 lb 8 oz. When she had been taken away to be tidied up, the student doctor took my hand and said, 'Thank you for a wonderful experience.' I will never forget that gesture.

Zoë was brought back, I put her to my breast and a nurse came in with cups of tea all round. Pauline had to get back to her family but Louise stayed with me until midnight.

In retrospect I realise how very much the success of Zoë's birth and my happy memory of it was dependent on a combination of factors: the wonderful support and understanding from Louise and Pauline, my classes and my early preparation through self-hypnosis. Also, the regional nursing officer who gave permission for two people to attend, instead of the usual one; my super midwife; the two students who assisted me during the second half of labour and the midwife who helped me so much through the difficult time when my baby was ill afterwards, and who cheered me up with her warm personality.

When I am asked about the birth and mention that I had no painkillers, the usual comment is, 'You were lucky you had no pain' or, 'There was no need to be a martyr.' I wanted to give Zoë the best possible advantage and it was fortunate that I did so. At birth she appeared to be a healthy, strong and alert baby, but two days later she was taken to the special care unit, after two severe spells of cyanosis. She is now a healthy, beautiful baby, and I love her very much.

Here is an account of the same labour from Pauline's point of view, which describes what she and Louise did that helped Charlotte meet the challenge of her labour so well.

Charlotte is coping very well and I tell her so – Louise is communicating with her as only a friend of long standing can and I stroke Charlotte's hand which is beginning to grip the arm of the chair – she instantly stops and smiles knowingly at me.

The time whizzes past; we apply the warm freezella pack wrapped in a dry flannel to Charlotte's sacrum. She is very hot so I put cool flannels at her wrists and the back of her neck. Out come the ice cubes for her to suck. Each gesture from us is rewarded with a warm smile from Charlotte and I am amazed at her control.

The midwife pops in and says Charlotte is doing well. The student doctor asks her if she wants an epidural – 'No thank you,' says Charlotte. The student midwives listen to the baby's heart beat and smile reassuringly.

The contractions are now coming every two and a half minutes and last one minute or one and a quarter minutes and I look at the clock. It is 6 p.m. Charlotte is using light breathing for most of the contraction and her eyes are looking slightly bloodshot – 'Gosh,' she says, 'this is hard work.' I think it is time she is examined but the hospital is busy and the midwife is nowhere around. The student midwife does not respond to my, 'I think Charlotte might find it helpful to be examined.' 'You are doing very well,' says the little midwife, and pats Charlotte's abdomen. The student doctor drifts off for his supper – it's obviously not exciting enough for him.

Charlotte is beginning to feel sick at the height of the contractions and finds this very hard to cope with – the cold flannel helps a little bit on the back of the neck and so do little sips of water.

We all decide a move on to the bed is a good idea – the nurse wants Charlotte to lie on her side but tactfully we manoeuvre Charlotte into a sitting position and the little nurse finds her lots of large pillows. Charlotte gives several little belches – 'Could this be transition?' I think.

It is 7 p.m. Charlotte says after a contraction, 'That one really hurt.' 'Ah ha,' says the nurse, 'that's how we want them to be – now they will be doing some good.' It's too much for me – I stick my neck out – 'This must be transition, Charlotte, keep it up it won't be long now.' (Oh, I hope I'm right) – but the signs are coming thick and fast now. Charlotte says she would give anything not to have another contraction – murmurs about gas and air and dozes off in between contractions. Finally the midwife says she thinks the baby will be born soon. 'I should think by 8 p.m.'. We all gasp with relief and our hearts lift.

They ask Charlotte to roll over. Louise helps her to breathe and the midwife sees a bulging anus. 'Soon you'll be able to push!'

Back to sitting position – Charlotte puts an arm round both our necks and we all blow out candles to cope with the strange semi wanting to push contractions – I want to giggle and am impressed with the composure of the midwife opposite to us. How funny we must look, the three of us all blowing in unison.

A senior, very motherly midwife comes in and is lovely. She tells Charlotte what a good girl she is, examines her briefly and says all right she can push.

Charlotte feels the contractions; after the last few hours of non-stop hectic activity the uterus seems to be less active and we have about five minutes of calm. It is like the eye of the hurricane. Here comes a contraction but the wave doesn't break; it swells up, dies back, but here it comes again and this time Charlotte can push. Oh, how well she does! 'Keep going,' we say.

The midwife tells Charlotte not to take such a big breath in the middle of the contraction and with the next push the head is seen like a wrinkled walnut. The midwives whisper to each other about how well Charlotte is doing – tell her, I think; why not tell her?

Now it is all activity – some students are called in to see, Charlotte is told to do exactly as the midwife says, and lifts her baby daughter on to her tummy.

Charlotte says, 'Oh, isn't she beautiful!' and I want to cry. Everyone is full of warmth and Charlotte is a queen.

A student nurse says to me, 'Now I don't mind having a baby.' The student doctor congratulates Charlotte on giving him a wonderful experience – the midwife who attended her is rosy with pleasure.

The baby is Zoë and she's beautiful.

And here is Louise's view of the birth

Charlotte signed up for Natural Childbirth classes, and I went along to three of them. I was interested in what I was learning and also embarrassed. I felt a funny feeling that 'I ought to know all this' and a strange feeling of wanting to be in touch with how Charlotte was feeling. She seemed to make sense of all the blowing and breathing exercises! This was a

196

fantastic rehearsal for me but I tried to imagine how men who are expecting children might feel. It seemed difficult to relate to what was going on – here was nature taking its course and I could do nothing about it – perhaps it was more that I felt there was no 'need' for me to do anything. Nonetheless, I felt somewhat useless. Despite being encouraged to go away and practise massage and breathing together, we didn't. It was partly due to embarrassment and also because I felt Charlotte could manage fine on her own, knowing I was there.

The special day grew nearer and nearer. I got more and more nervous waiting for the phone to ring. Every time I was away from a phone I imagined Charlotte had had her baby. I felt very restricted – I couldn't go out anywhere like the pictures for fear of her phoning to say she was in labour. In many ways I hated the great feeling of responsibility and felt guilty because of that. I wondered how husbands and boyfriends coped with it all – hearing about nothing but babies. Sometimes I thought it would drive me mad if I was actually living with Charlotte; then there was the side of me that felt extremely proud of what was happening and exceptionally lucky to be able to share such a personal experience.

10.30 p.m. on Thursday night. The phone rang, 'I think this is it,' said Charlotte. Her contractions had started. I gathered up my bag of tricks: flasks for ice cubes; natural sponges to suck water through; fruit juices and mineral water. I had been in bed when Charlotte called but my adrenalin immediately gave me tons of energy. This was like getting ready for a picnic or preparing for a magic voyage! . . .

Pauline and Louise turn up in the delivery suite 'looking like a couple of charwomen! Baggy white gowns, paper mop hats and plastic bags over our shoes!'

6.14 p.m. on Friday. We'd been going for nearly four hours now – solid non-stop concentration. I remember feeling exhausted myself and wondering how on earth Charlotte had the strength to go on.

We were left alone a lot of the time. I found myself a good job to do, and that was massaging Charlotte's feet with talcum powder. During one contraction I'd stopped and all that Charlotte could do was make frantic noises and point madly at her feet for me to start again ...

The staff put on green gowns and masks. Here's a really nice midwife, she's helping and explaining a lot and she thinks the labour has been so splendid that she asks if a group of trainees can watch the delivery. 'But of course! The more the merrier.'

Our attention is focused so intensely between Charlotte's legs and on quick, quick, quick, quick, quick breaths. Any minute now something's going to happen! The expectancy and excitement in the air are so electric. My eyes practically pop out in disbelief every time Charlotte's whole stomach goes into a great big heave, like a massive tidal wave and it's as solid as concrete. 'Look, Charlotte, look!'

Black hair – a head is coming out. It's crying!

Flop back against the pillows for a rest, then we're pushing again. 'Come on, Charlotte, help your baby out. Stretch forward and lift it.' This is unbelievable, a baby, a person, a human being, it's a girl! We were really convinced it would be a boy. Zoë!

I really thought I'd cry when the baby was actually born. I didn't. I felt grounded, as if centred by it – it was so amazing. Yet it felt absolutely right.

Zoë was immaculate. She opened her eyes almost straight away and looked incredibly alert. We had to agree that it must have had a lot to do with keeping healthy during the pregnancy and not using any drugs whatsoever during labour.

A PERSISTENT OCCIPITO-POSTERIOR DELIVERY

This mother found it difficult to relax the abdominal wall during pregnancy, and her doctor mentioned this particularly in his letter. She was so tense that she was difficult to examine. She was particularly anxious about how she would relax in labour – especially since we knew beforehand that the baby was posterior.

My labour started on Sunday at 11.30 in the evening. The contractions lasted about two minutes with five- or six-minute intervals. This continued all night and at 5.30 a.m. I woke my husband. We continued timing contractions for an hour, then called the doctor and nurse, only to learn that they were already out. They came later and the nurse examined me and said I was five centimetres dilated. But then everything stopped. In the evening I went to bed. The doctor gave me a sleeping pill so that I should have the energy to cope with things the next day, but still nothing much happened and I worked like a mad thing all day. (I could, from time to time, feel contractions if I put my hands on my tummy). Once again I woke at 11.30 p.m. to find the contractions had returned in earnest, this time coming every three minutes. They gradually got stronger and faster, and I found the shallow breathing a great help. I woke my husband at 1.30 a.m. and he called the nurse, who arrived at 2.10 a.m. She examined me and said I could start pushing, but I said I didn't feel ready to. So we waited, but not many minutes passed before I found I had to do so. (It worried me a bit beforehand if I would recognise the signs, but I found there was no chance of mistaking the feeling!)

My baby was lying back to front, and you warned me that

I might have a long second stage and an anterior lip. Both of these happened, and the nurse was quite surprised to find I was expecting it. She offered me an injection, but I still said no. The doctor arrived, but I'm not sure when as I lost all sense of time although I had a clock in front of me. I was on my back. I found this was the best way as I had backache, and needed a pillow in the small of my back to ease the pain. I also found that my left leg had gone completely numb and I couldn't move it at all myself. This was a bit annoying, but the doctor held my foot and moved it for me when needed. I began to feel very hot and my head felt as thought it would burst. I felt weary and was quite sure that if something didn't happen soon I wouldn't have the strength to go on. Then I remembered that you said the end was getting near when one began to feel desperate, and this cheered me up, and I continued with fresh determination.

At this point the doctor said I should try some gas-and-air as I was so tired, and that I need not continue with it if I didn't want to, so I tried it, and it helped me enormously. I stayed completely alert and obeyed instructions. The doctor told me to take a deep breath as the contractions started, count, and push on three, but I found this was the only thing I couldn't do. Push I could, but count I could not. So my husband counted for me, and all was well. He was with me the whole time and was a great comfort and help. He wiped my face with a cold flannel and reassured me that I was doing fine. Both of these helped so much! I found I could get two or three pushes each time.

After a few minutes the nurse told me to roll on my side. She said I must as the babe was still facing the wrong way and it would be safer, so over I went, but what an effort! I felt glued to the bed! I felt terribly hot and was told that the room must be kept warm for the baby as he was almost there.

At the crowning I found panting helped when the nurse told me not to push. He crowned, and as his head slipped out he yelled lustily, and my husband announced that *he* had dark hair. I couldn't see him crown as I was on my side, but

I did see the rest of him born. He came very easily with one more gentle push. It was wonderful and I felt so clever! It was 5.35 a.m. when my son was born, and he weighed $8\frac{1}{2}$ lb.

Immediately after the birth I felt cold and shivered madly although the room was very warm. To add to the fun there was an urgent call for the doctor about ten minutes before the babe was born so as soon as it was over he rushed off.

The babe's head when born was pushed into a most odd shape but was soon quite normal. When they let me hold him the afterbirth came at once, ten minutes after the birth. Soon we were put tidy and I enjoyed a cup of tea (the best ever).

My summing up of the whole thing was how well the word 'labour' fitted. It was jolly hard work but well worth while. I asked the doctor afterwards if he thought the classes had helped, and he said I couldn't have coped as well as I did if I hadn't attended them. I enjoyed the classes and felt no worry about my coming confinement. Thanks to the very full explanations, nothing came as a surprise, I recognised each stage as it arrived, and I felt happy the whole time.

A CHINESE RESTAURANT AND A ROCKING CHAIR

This was a second baby after a previous unpleasant labour lasting 45 hours, with maternal exhaustion and foetal distress. Shortly before the baby was due this woman said to me, 'I'm afraid that when I go into labour I shall panic because I shall think, "Oh my God, it's happening again".' She had sinusitis in the last weeks of this pregnancy, and wondered whether she would be able to manage the breathing.

Andrew was born at 3.33 p.m. last Friday and weighed 6 lb 15 oz.

I went to the antenatal clinic the previous afternoon at 4.00 and after doing an internal examination the doctor said he thought the baby would be born within the next 48 hours. In fact he thought I would just have time to shut the shop and pack my bag!

Naturally I was very excited and went home and did all sorts of last-minute jobs. At about 6.30 p.m. I started very mild contractions, like period pains, at five-minute intervals. My husband decided we should go out for dinner, so we went to a Chinese restaurant about five minutes walk away. This was about 8.15 p.m. During the walk I had to stop twice and my husband wondered if we should turn back, but I thought contractions would slow down when I sat, and this proved to be the case. They were coming every five minutes and were strong enough to make me want to stop eating or talking and take fairly deep breaths. I wasn't very hungry and by 9.00 p.m. wanted to get home. We had to stop three times on the way back. I then sat in a rocking chair for about half an hour, which was very comfortable, and went on doing fairly deep breathing during contractions, which were lasting about 30 seconds each.

At 9.45 p.m. I had a warm bubble-bath with my husband in close attendance, and got into bed at 10.20 p.m. with a hot water bottle and an interesting book. I soon went to sleep, and for the next hour and a half slept between contractions, but managed to rouse myself each time, and met them with shallow chest breathing. They were much stronger and lasted about 40 seconds. At midnight I went to the lavatory and decided on my return to bed to stay awake to cope efficiently. I did this for an hour without any appreciable change in the character of the contractions, but sleep overcame me once more and for two hours I returned to the pattern of sleeping in between. However it was now becoming more difficult to rouse myself.

At 3.00 a.m. I went downstairs and woke my husband who was sleeping on the living-room sofa so as to be ready when needed. I said I couldn't go on by myself, so he made a cup of tea and returned upstairs with me. I got back into bed and then for an hour went on with contractions lasting 45–50 seconds at four- to five-minute intervals. At 4.00 a.m. I decided I ought to go to the hospital, and we went downstairs and having sat down for a while in the rocking chair in front of the fire I was so comfortable I went off to sleep again! My husband dozed too, but I was able to wake to meet the contractions and woke him so that he could time them. By 6.00 a.m. they were coming about every four minutes and lasting anything up to a minute and a half, so we went to the hospital –whereupon nothing happened for about twenty minutes.(1)

From the time I left the house until I had had all the reception procedures of shaving, showering and suppositories there wasn't a contraction worthy of the name. The Sister examined me externally and *per rectum* and said I was 'labouring nicely' but it would be 'some time' before I had the baby. She then gave me an injection of pethidine.

From 7.45 a.m. until 10.30 a.m. I experienced the classic consequences of sedation, dreaming in between contractions, and then having to make a great effort to meet them. None-theless I was able to do this by shallow breathing and rubbing the small of my back with my left hand. This coped quite adequately with even 'double-peak' contractions.

At about 10.30 a.m. during a routine examination of the foetal heart I felt sick and vomited fluid. I was put on a glucose drip. This put my left hand out of action, so I turned on my left side and rubbed my back with my other hand. I was never left for long, and I remember at one point the Sister telling a pupil midwife that I had been trained by Mrs K. and was doing my breathing properly. My husband came back then, but could only stay a short while, but rubbed my back for me which was a great comfort. All the nurses were very good about leaving one alone during contractions and also gave every help in the way of massage. I found the staff exceptionally kind. Sister was so encouraging and very patient. Nothing was spared in the way of cool drinks and having my face cooled.

At 1.30 p.m. I was moved into the delivery room. I was still entirely in control. Sister sent someone to keep me company, and then at 1.50 p.m. she did an internal exam. She offered me gas-and-air for this, but I didn't need it at all, and said so. She said I was very relaxed and this made her task much easier. She had noticed how relaxed I had been throughout.

She found there was a slight anterior lip. I cheered up then, and one of the pupils stayed with me all the time. The whole prolonged first stage had been hardly at all painful. At 2.30 p.m. I had the first strong urge to push. I was transferred to the delivery bed. My husband came in then. When the next contraction came I was lying right over on my right side and I realised that this was *not* a helpful position and was really an attempt on my part to withdraw, as it were, from the situation. I got my husband to pull me up into a sitting position with by back supported, and this had the effect of giving me a more positive attitude to the whole business. The next few contractions were very strong but I managed to push as instructed, without gas and air. Once or twice I realised that my face was grimaced and tense, but I was able to correct this and concentrate efforts lower down. It took three or four big contractions to get the head round the corner and visible to the midwife. After two more contractions the head crowned, and I had the burning and splitting sensation which you mentioned. I remember sweating at that point, but all the same I was still aware that my own efforts were of paramount importance. Sister reminded me of the short breaths at the crowning. (I had a slight tear needing two stitches.) Two more contractions and Andrew arrived all in a rush. He was held up and roared lustily. The after-birth arrived (in about three minutes).

Note

1. This quite often happens, and the woman can feel guilty because she 'ought' to be having contractions.

CHILDBIRTH ... A SOCIAL ACT

I am grateful for many things, but I think particularly your emphasis on the husband's part, and the advantages of a home confinement. I don't know how much freedom husbands have in hospital delivery rooms but I feel certain Bruce would have been inhibited by the hospital 'ambience', and my sister, who was also with me all the time, would presumably not have been allowed. When she asked if she might be with me during labour – particularly delivery – I was definitely doubtful. I talked about it with Bruce and the midwife, and decided that I would make no decision till labour was under way. I should say that the chief reason I had for not wanting her with me was a selfish one: I thought the birth should be something between Bruce and me alone, something I did not want to share even with a much loved sister, yet part of me wanted to share it with her, and I think Miss F. (the midwife) strengthened this. I grew to feel that childbirth is a social act and would be a co-operative effort.

The baby was due on Friday. For two months it had been lying on the left (left occiput lateral). Then it turned L.O.A., but later it changed to R.O.P. You can imagine that I was annoyed about this, as I knew that L.O.A. was the most favourable position and R.O.P. meant a long first stage and backache. I rushed off from the surgery to the library to do some hard work to ward off the blues.

We had spent a happy day with my sister and a friend picnicking in the Gloucestershire countryside, admiring Chipping Campden church and a beautiful National Trust garden. We got home at 8.00 p.m., had dinner and went to bed at about 11.00 p.m. For the first time in about three or four weeks I had not had a rest during the day. At 11.30 p.m.

I felt a strong contraction – stronger than any of the powerful Braxton-Hicks I had had during the last weeks. Five or ten minutes later the waters broke, and I had another contraction about two minutes later. I rang Miss F. who said she would send her pupil, Miss S., to see me. She would examine me and give me a sedative if things appeared to be moving slowly (as I had had no sleep) and would let Miss F. know how I was.

I felt very excited. I hugged Bruce with joy when the waters broke and called out to Priscilla, 'It's started!' She rushed out of her bedroom looking delighted. Miss S. arrived at 2.15 a.m. and between then and ringing Miss F. I had contractions at 11.48, 11.54, 12.00, 12.05, 12.10, 12.16. They were easy to cope with doing deep chest breathing but I was surprised at their length. They appeared sometimes to last two minutes and usually at least one and a half minutes. In between contractions I rushed about getting things ready, but lay on the bed during most of these contractions – they demanded it. Miss S. talked of giving me a sedative, and asked what your views on sedation were as she was keen to fit in with my training. I was longing to relax between contractions. She said that she would give me an enema. I said that my bowels had worked twice that day. Nothing more was said about the enema. The contractions speeded up, coming at three-minute intervals. Miss S. was filling my card and preparing equipment and I was trying hard not to be resentful of her for not being Miss F! She is a most charming girl, whom I had met several times at the clinic and once at home with Miss F. I should have *hated* to hurt her feelings. She was very encouraging about my breathing, telling me I was coping well, which I felt I was.

She and Priscilla began to prepare the bed and the baby's cot. Bruce had to leave me for a moment and the contractions seemed painful and so *long*. Suddenly I realised that the time for deep chest breathing had passed, and went straight into shallow rapid breathing. What a relief! How thankful I was for the hours of practice I had put into this breathing. I was right on top of things. Bruce was rubbing my back most comfortingly. The bed being prepared, I came thankfully to it and lay in the left lateral so that Bruce could rub my aching back.

Contractions came harder and faster and there never seemed to be any pause between them, though I presume there was. I had no difficulty at all in adjusting my breathing to the rhythm of the contractions and I was completely relaxed. I enjoyed the feeling of the firm bed under me; it seemed to me that I was lying on the earth, close to it. I disliked the pain but never felt it would master me. Bruce continued to rub my back, which I craved.

As the end of the first stage approached my mouth was bone dry and I was terribly hot. My long hair clung to my face and my brushed nylon nightdress was much too hot. I wish I had had time to change into the simple cotton garment I had bought specially for the occasion and to pull my hair back from my face with an elastic band. Priscilla managed to help me do these two tasks. She gave me ice to suck and a hot drink, and she bathed my face and neck in water. I remember sucking the flannel with relief. She was wonderfully calm (she had already read *The Experience of Childbirth* and seen a birth film). People kept telling me how well I was doing. This surprised me. It seemed so automatic. It was almost as odd as if someone suddenly said to me, 'How *well* you are breathing today.'

I had a bad moment. A hot water bottle which was burning hot was placed against my back and I was at the height of a contraction but managed to gasp 'too hot'.

Miss S. asked if I would 'like anything' (medication) and I said, 'No' without hesitation. I kept repeating to myself, 'I greet every contraction with my breathing.' This helped to keep up my spirits and energy for the hard work, especially as the feeling of pressure low down increased in intensity.

Suddenly the desire to bear down began to establish itself. I was so glad that you had said that it felt like wanting to pass a big motion. That's just what it's like. I am sure that, but for

208

the training, I should never have recognised it for what it was, and should have been distressed at wanting to go to the lavatory, and perhaps have struggled to get up. I told Miss S. I felt like bearing down but could control it and asked if she thought I should. She said I should and at once told Priscilla to phone Miss F. and tell her. The urge was quite controllable and I did a little blowing out. I was still in the left lateral. However I was comfortable and hoped I might see something of the birth in the mirror. Bruce was experimenting with the mirror when Miss F. (who told me afterwards she had been quite astonished at Priscilla's phone call) came in. I was so pleased to see her. She examined me and I heard her say to Miss S., 'You see, you could never teach a woman to breathe like that while she is actually *in labour*.' In two ticks she had me up on the wedge [1] and I was told to bear down. It was about 2.30 a.m.

Miss F. was so clear and encouraging in her directions about how much to push with each contraction, and I followed her exactly. It was so exciting seeing the first glimpse of Oliver's vernix-coated head. (I was surprised at the bright yellowness.) I enjoyed the second stage – particularly from a social aspect – it was real team work – and I was so proud of Bruce. He was so happy looking and kept reminding me to smile, and a few times I caught sight of my face in the glass and was delighted to see that I was happy and smiling.

The head crowned with a burning feeling and I was told to breathe it out. Miss F. said to Miss S. 'I'm glad you can see this.' I found it quite easy, perhaps because the urge to bear down never seemed overwhelming. I saw a little blood trickle down.

While I was still panting lightly the baby's head shot out. It was 3.00 a.m. I saw its face, which was like a white clay mask. In a few seconds all of it was out and on my stomach, and I was filled with tremendous relief and elation at having

1. These are foam wedge-shaped cushions obtainable from The National Childbirth Trust, 9 Queensborough Terrace, London, W2 3TB.

experienced this exciting shared birth. He was wrapped and handed screaming to me to hold him, and I was pleased to hold him but my main emotions were of huge gratitude to my attendants and a feeling of tremendous achievement in labour. I thanked them all with joy and told them how happy I was. Bruce was so delighted to have a boy. I handed Oliver to him almost at once and Bruce, who had never handled a baby, took him gladly and confidently. He was more thrilled with him than I was. I felt just the same towards him as when he was in the womb and very real to me after the quickening. It was only about five hours after the birth that I loved him in the real sense of love, not in the detached way one loves the womb-child. I was brought to love him like this: Bruce was sitting beside me and we were wondering whether to pick him up or not as he was making whimpering noises. Bruce's eyes filled with tears – a very rare thing with him. He was so moved by the pathetic helplessness of the child. Something in me was released. I turned away from my somewhat egotistic involvement in my labour towards my child, and since that moment my love has grown so that both of us are now in love with him – so much that it actually hurts sometimes. Could Bruce ever have felt like that if he had not experienced my fully conscious prepared labour and delivery and helped me achieve it?

I was surprised when Miss F. told me I had torn and went to ring up Dr F. She said there was nothing I could possibly have done to prevent it. The baby never rotated. I didn't mind about the tear. Bruce said afterwards he felt sad when he saw the tissue give way, but realised I didn't know. Miss F. suggested Bruce might like to leave the room, but he looked so unhappy I asked if he might stay as he obviously would prefer to. You will have heard of scores of squeamish husbands who suddenly lost their squeamishness at a prepared childbirth; well, Bruce is yet another. He has always hated talk of disease or injury and the only thing he didn't like about my training with you was the occasional tale of forceps, placentas that stayed put, etc. which I brought back on Wednesdays. But he didn't mind watching Dr F. stitch me. I was completely relaxed. My stitches are out now and I have got back control of the pelvic floor already.

Dr F. congratulated me as soon as he came in. Miss F. had told him I had done very well.

Oliver weighed 7 lb 12 oz. The relaxation exercises are wonderfully useful in breast-feeding, making one aware of one's tension. I had a hard time helping Oliver to 'fix'. Miss S. gave me hours of her time and we are feeding very successfully now. He is a most contented, calm, sweet child. We took some photographs when he was three hours old. I should also like to come and show Oliver off and answer questions at the next class. I always found that aspect of your classes such fun and very helpful.

What exciting days these have been! How we have savoured them! The birth details have been talked over endlessly between us. It was unforgettable.

CALM, COOL AND COLLECTED

This mother was herself a nurse; she was in a hospital whose midwives are usually very understanding and helpful. But they are human! Sometimes, they, too, have off days, and in this account the mother copes with a situation in which communication has more or less broken down.

Although my first two pregnancies were not a nightmare, a friend persuaded me to have Natural Childbirth classes with my third pregnancy. This was well worthwhile as this account of my experience should be proof enough.

To begin with, I would stress that pregnant women should attend a relaxation class run by adequately trained persons, as just breathing deeply and panting are not quite enough. Instruction on the anatomy and physiology of the pregnant mother-to-be is very important I think, as it helps to ensure a relaxed and happy mental approach to what, after all, is the most wonderful experience in a woman's life.

The last two months went by very slowly. Then at last the end was in sight – I awoke at 3.00 a.m. with contractions strong enough to wake me from a deep sleep. Breathing as I was taught, I soon relaxed, and was able to nod off intermittently until day-break. I was so excited! By about noon, my contractions became more frequent. At this point my husband took me to the nursing home. After all the formalities of 'booking in' I was left in peace. My contractions became less frequent so I began to walk up and down and around to encourage them.

During the course of the evening when the contractions became more regular I was constantly being offered pethidine, as they decided that I was tiring myself with 'all that breathing' and would have no strength left to produce the baby when the time came! I declined their offers gracefully and tried to get some sleep.

Just after midnight I awoke with strong contractions. Not wanting to disturb the only nurse on duty unless necessary, I brought my breathing into practice and tried to think of all sorts of things – what will it be and what shall we name it and what was going on inside of me. All this took a fair amount of concentration. My husband was sent home, so I was on my own. At last I decided the time had come, and pressed the bell. Here I must pause to say that at the time I was suffering from retro-bulbar neuritis, which is an inflammation of the optic nerve resulting in almost total blindness. My doctor was fairly concerned and had asked to be telephoned immediately if I 'started'. The nurse eventually appeared and examined me. I asked her to ring my husband too. She then left to telephone the doctor and to fetch the trolley on which I was to be transported to the delivery room.

During her long absence the membranes broke. I knew then that it would not be long and pressed the bell once more. She arrived armed with the trolley which she manoeuvred alongside my bed and casually ordered me to 'hop on'. As I was at the height of a contraction, I continued to pant. She repeated her order. As the contraction subsided, I took the opportunity to crawl from a rather damp bed on to the trolley. As she pushed me down the corridor, I had another two or three contractions, thus giving birth to the baby's head – quietly! I told the nurse what had happened, as I felt very pleased with myself. She stopped the trolley instantly and had a 'peep', covered me quickly and said, 'Nonsense, you haven't screamed!' I was amazed at her denial so I continued the conversation no further.

We arrived at the delivery room. She pushed the trolley beside the delivery bed and once more ordered me to 'hop on' and went off to scrub up.

Bewildered for a few moments, I then decided that it wasn't worth an argument, and somehow wriggled on to the delivery bed supporting the baby's head with one hand and with the other edging my way on to the bed. I do not think I could do it again, but I was so full of confidence!

The nurse by this time had returned (all scrubbed) in time to deliver the tail end of Perdita – my gorgeous 6 lb 5 oz baby girl.

Before even cutting the umbilical cord she rushed off to open the front door for the doctor, who had been ringing the door bell for the past ten minutes. All the drama was over, but he was the first to offer his congratulations.

I was extremely thankful that I had been prepared so well during my pregnancy, as I don't think that I would have enjoyed my confinement quite so much. My only regret was the absence of my husband, who would have completed the scene.

A TINGLING FEELING – NOT UNPLEASANT

Julian's birth has been a wonderful experience for both of us.

7.00 a.m. A show which continued all day.

2.00 p.m. Contractions started at fifteen-minute intervals. We did the weekend shopping.

4.00 p.m. Contractions now at seven-minute intervals. No special breathing was necessary for any of them.

6.00 p.m. Had a hot bath. Contractions stopped!

10.00 p.m. Contractions restarted at fifteen-minute intervals. We dozed until . . .

1.20 a.m. . . . when the contractions were about every five minutes and strong enough to wake me with sensations in the lower abdomen. We decided to get up and prepare everything and drank black coffee to wake ourselves up properly. For these contractions I began deep chest breathing, and the unpleasant stretching sensation was immediately relieved.

2.30 a.m. We now had everything ready and I lay down on the bed next to the wedge which we had arranged in position for the second stage. Jeff got your recommended three hot water bottles, and with plenty of pillows I became very comfortable.

3.00 a.m. Contractions stronger and at three-minute intervals.

4.00 a.m. Contractions at two-and-a-half-minute intervals and lasting one-and-a-half minutes.

4.10 a.m. Contractions being felt low down in the back.

5.00 a.m. Contractions at one-and-a-half to two-minute intervals. I got on to the wedge as we both thought the transition stage couldn't be far away. I was using upper chest breathing and feeling well on top of contractions

215

and able to 'cut the corners'. Soon after this I began to use the Russian technique(1) to relieve backache during contractions.

7.30 a.m. No change. My sister-in-law (an obstetrician) arrived. She examined me internally and said I was more than six centimetres dilated, the membrances were tight over the head and she was unable to repture them with her fingers. She was most impressed at my relaxation and breathing during contractions. She recommended that we phone the midwife. This we did at 8.00 a.m.

8.30 a.m. The midwife arrived with student and immediately asked Jeff to leave the room while she examined me. We both said we'd prefer him to stay. Fortunately things were more ready than she had expected, and when we showed her the wedge and the way we had arranged the bed she told the student that she could do a dorsal delivery. From that moment she was very helpful and pleasant. We showed her your book which seemed to interest her, particularly the chapter on husbands, and this at once changed her attitude to Jeff.

By now the student and midwife had both examined me internally, and the midwife tried during two contractions to rupture the membrances with her fingers. During a third contraction at . . .

9.10 a.m. . . . she succeeded, using a pair of forceps. The membranes were very tight over the baby's head. After rupturing the membranes the contractions almost immediately became much stronger although at longer intervals (two minutes). I was offered sedation but felt I was coping well and did not want anything.

From 9.45 a.m. until 10 a.m. I experienced backache which was more uncomfortable than the contractions and which persisted between contractions. During this period I found it difficult to maintain relaxation. The nature of the contractions now seemed to be changing and at 9.55 a.m. I asked if I could push. When encouraged to do so I did only halfheartedly for two or three contractions, and these were most uncomfortable. I then regained complete control, largely due to Jeff's help and directions and started to make good use of each contraction.

10.00 a.m. The head was first visible and . . .

10.15 a.m. . . . Julian was born, 7 lb 12 oz. For two contractions I panted to control the birth of the head, as I could tell by the feel of the perineum that this was necessary. The student asked me to pant only for the second contraction when I was already doing so energetically! The head was born slowly and easily, the sensation being one of extreme stretching and a tingling, burning feeling. This was not at all unpleasant, although I can easily imagine that one could panic if unprepared for these sensations. I was well propped up on the wedge and able to see the birth easily and found the delivery most exciting. The second stage had lasted 20 minutes.

He cried immediately, was wrapped in a nappy and the midwife then handed him to Jeff to give to me. This we thought was very thoughtful of her.

The placenta was delivered fifteen minutes after the birth and the blood loss was approximately 6 oz.

We were interested to note how very alert and bright Julian was immediately after the birth, and subsequently. I went to the bathroom the same day, came downstairs the following day, and have remained very active ever since, feeling extremely well. The height of the fundus went down extremely quickly, much to the amazement of the midwife who also commented that I didn't look as if I'd had a baby!

Note

1. This involves lying on the fists so that there is firm pressure on the points where the pelvis joins the spine over the side of the sacrum.

FIRST ACT AT THE PANTOMIME

Mark arrived on Tuesday at noon, and were we glad to see him. All 9 lb 8 oz of him!

We looked back on it with an immense amount of pleasure and satisfaction, as well as a tremendous sense of achievement, but perhaps I'd better start at the beginning!

The presentation before labour started was L.O.P., and I was depressed and rather impatient for the birth. I attacked the house. Then the doctor arrived and did an internal (he stretched the cervix slightly). Nurse came and I had castor oil and later – at 4.30 p.m. – an enema. Nothing regular was happening, so a few hours after this she left. Things stopped completely at 8.00 p.m. and I took a sleeping pill and we went to bed.

I was woken with three-minute contractions at about 2.00 a.m. We fetched nurse and she came and made all the paper bags. These contractions continued at three-minute intervals through the night, getting fiercer towards dawn. However at 7.00 a.m. I was still not dilating! This was disappointing, as we were feeling pleased to be in control; in fact it was a wonderful sensation of co-operation with one's body. However I was then given a sedative and went to sleep and nurse departed. The next day nothing happened. Again we went to bed *very* early and slept!

On Monday we decided to go to the pantomime to cheer ourselves up! During the afternoon I felt odd contractions, and put them down to castor oil, I'd given up hope of all else! Anyway, off we went. We enjoyed ourselves, although I was uncomfortable at times because when one laughs it seems to coincide with any contractions which happen to be around! We got back and decided things weren't regular enough for it to be labour so I took a sleeping pill. This seems to have been a mistake, as I awoke at 1.00 a.m. and couldn't decide what was happening, except that I was either having a nightmare or was in pain! When my husband had (with much sternness!) calmed me down, we timed contractions and found they were remarkably strong (shallow chest breathing) and at ten- to seven-minute intervals. We fetched poor nurse again and she got here at 2.30 a.m. She rushed around and then did an internal, reporting that half an hour should see full dilatation. Contractions got quicker and stronger but the cervix didn't dilate any more (there was a lip). At 7.00 a.m. I was still in perfect control and we were not feeling tired, but nurse said she thought the uterus was getting tired and pethidine might quicken things up. I agreed to have a 50 mg. shot of the stuff and was quite glad I did.

Doctor came at 8.30 a.m. and said he thought we'd have a baby by lunchtime! He congratulated us on managing so well. Things still went well, and I couldn't decide why a doctor appeared at about 11.15 a.m. just as the transition stage was in progress. It lasted from 10.00 a.m. till 11.30 a.m. It was very difficult as the waters went so suddenly and the shivering started. I think I lost control, but everyone seems to think everything went O.K. The baby's head didn't drop at all, so when the second stage started he had a long journey. The second stage began around 11.30 a.m. and this was hard work. Mark emerged at 11.55 a.m. and I saw his head in the mirror from the first sight of the very tip of it to the birth – a *great* help. The placenta came spontaneously five minutes after the baby. We didn't have any sugar loaf moulding. Although he was posterior he turned himself at the very end. He really is a darling and *so* sweet and good. Breast-feeding is going very well.

I was glad I didn't know, but doctor told my husband that I might have to be a hospital delivery and they had alerted the hospital for a forceps delivery. However all is well and it really is satisfying! I was so glad I'd made the effort to come to classes. They really are a help!

219

DAWN CHORUS AND CHAMPAGNE

This mother had been a midwife. Some days before she actually went into labour she had a 'false labour', with irregular contractions all day, but after going to bed and deciding that she was settling down to sleep, they stopped.

We had an enjoyable dinner out on E.D.D. (1) and the next day went to a party, which certainly did us good.

The next day, having vague feelings of impending labour – not really 'nesting',(2) just wishful thinking perhaps, at 10.00 p.m. contractions started, coming at ten-minute intervals – with a fair amount of backache. By 12 midnight the contractions were stronger and at five-minute intervals. But I still wasn't convinced it was labour – no show or anything to complain about. My husband then woke and took command! I was ordered into a bath I didn't really want, but *did* enjoy. Then we settled down to some relaxing and back rubbing, and contractions by 2.00 a.m. were down to every three minutes, but only lasting thirty to forty-five seconds. At last, a show. So my husband rang the midwife, who eventually came at 2.40 a.m. We had all the things in our room but boiled up the saucepan and did various last-minute things. The contractions were getting rather sharp but still very short. The baby's head was rotating from the posterior to the anterior. The nurse, who is very sweet, got her equipment organised. I was just sitting in a chair – and doing some mouth-centred breathing. The midwife said to my husband while I was in the bathroom, 'It will be some time yet, the contractions are so short.'

However at 3.50 a.m. I felt a real urge to push, but thinking of posterior positions decided it couldn't be, and carried

220

on breathing and blowing. After the next contraction I just had to say, 'I think it's coming.' The midwife said, 'Ooh, I don't think so,' but I got on to the bed (just finished being prepared) and had a contraction, and she said, 'You're right.' I continued to breathe and blow. My husband came up after I'd banged on the floor for him, and afterwards admitted he thought I was fussing about his presence rather early! But then he realised that the baby was about to be born. With the next contration I felt baby's head well down, and I 'breathed-down' and the nurse ruptured the membranes. With the next contraction, with my husband cheering me on, I pushed a little, was told to pant, so did mouth-centred breathing – a bit more pushing – more mouth-centred breathing – and then the head was born! The cord was round the baby's neck and had to be cut, so I did more mouth-centred breathing and blowing, as I felt I wanted to push it all out, which at last I did with the final part of that contraction. And there was our 'Dawn Chorus' – Sally, 7 lb at 3.15 a.m. She was beautifully pink and cried right away, and although wrinkled at that time had somehow 'unfolded' by 4.00 a.m.

We all then said how quick and wonderful it was. I held Sally and waited for the placenta, which came in ten minutes, and was fine. Total blood was only 4 oz.

It was a night of surprises. I was so amazed on being cleaned up when Nurse D. said, 'I don't think you'll need any stitches.'

I was sure she had done an episiotomy, when in fact I'd seen her take a forcep to rupture the membranes. This was such good news!

The rest of the early morn was rather more leisurely. I was made comfortable. Veronica [her other little daughter] awoke at 4.00 a.m. and heard crying and was thrilled to bits with 'her baby'. We drank champagne and toasted everyone at 4.45 a.m. and we still seem to be in that rather wonderful dreamy state – so thankful that all is well, and so pleased with ourselves! Looking back it was so quick – I only managed to have one suck at my barley sugar stick, and my forehead wiped with icy water once too. No real transitional stage. But best of all, and I only realised at the end, no pethidine or gas – which I didn't want – because breathing helped so much.

Breast-feeding is going so well, and she's a good, rhythmical sucker!

If only all women in the country could have this preparation, what a happier place labour wards would be, and the old ideas of grim labours would soon die out!

Notes

1. The expected date of delivery.
2. She is referring to the impulse, common to many women, to clean the house and start energetically sorting out cupboards, tidying drawers or painting furniture, the day or so before they go into labour.

GENTLE BIRTH

My second baby was born in hospital after desperate efforts to have a home delivery. My first labour had been unsympathetically managed and I could hardly bear the prospects of being taken over again by a hospital regime. Sadly, a retained placenta didn't assist my cause and at seven months I finally accepted that I would have to go through it all again. However, I took care to find a consultant who was completely sympathetic to the sort of birth I wanted – to give birth to my baby by my own efforts with no interference until his expert help was needed. I was astonished that he even offered me a Leboyer delivery – something I could not in my wildest dreams have hoped for. We discussed this type of delivery and agreed to adapt it to suit us. We decided to opt out of the bathing of the new born baby because Mr W. was worried about heat loss and the difficulty of maintaining the exact water temperature and I was not keen on the idea of someone else enjoying my baby when I was dying to. So, basically, the birth environment would be calm and caring and without violence. I had made what plans I could – the rest was up to nature.

Labour started, on the exact day, in the early hours of the morning. I crept out of bed and lay on the sofa in the kitchen and savoured the exhilaration of knowing that this long-awaited event had arrived. Time flew by, I felt confident and tried to be casual about the length and time of the contractions, knowing that there was still a long way to go. Eventually, sensing a cold and empty half of the bed my husband appeared and cosseted me in a way which only a man whose wife is in labour can. At first he was anxious and I was interested that the contractions were much more uncomfortable with his anxious face peering at me through the semi-darkness. But, at the same time, to feel the baby being pushed strongly down during each contraction was a positive and thrilling reminder of what was happening. I was four or five hours into labour now and feeling that we should be making a move so, after giving our two-and-a-half-year-old her breakfast and settling her with a friend, we set off. St Mary's is fairly informal, you are not shaved and can choose whether to have a bath, shower or not. After the admittance procedures my husband and I were re-united in a single labour room where he set up shop with his invaluable supply of ice chips for me to suck and beer and sandwiches for him. My breathing was going well. A little encouragement goes a long way and when the midwife said I was coping well I felt boosted. In contrast to my first labour I was surprised how aware I felt and how consciously I could lie relaxed around my contracting uterus and will my baby on its way. The membranes were still intact and when the contractions started to slow down, the midwife seemed to feel that rupturing them would speed things up again. I was also beginning to feel that speed was not a bad idea, but Mr W. had not yet arrived and it was written in my notes that the membranes were to be left, so I was nature-bound and things would take their own course.

Eventually I was admitted to the delivery room, still sucking ice and 'wearing' my frozen ice bag on my forehead. The lights were dimmed and the atmosphere quiet, just the two of us, the consultant and the midwife. I was rather beginning to wish that I hadn't passed off the instructions for using gas and oxygen so lightly but suddenly I was seized by the urge to push and found myself alert and revitalised, pulling myself up on the pillows and with unhurried concentration went through the pushing routine I had practised in National Childbirth Trust classes. The first push was very controlled and successful, at the second I was thrown by the consultant's shoulder against my foot, I let the third ride and after three or four more, with a lot of strangely comforting puffing

224

and grunting in between, and the enormous sensations of a baby in the birth canal, the head crowned.

When her body emerged she was laid across my abdomen, (the cord was unusually short and I couldn't hold her in my arms) she hardly cried and was very undistressed and unperturbed; the cord was cut when it had stopped pulsating. She just let us hold her and looked around peacefully and was quite content and we felt very moved by her. She sucked vigorously at the breast after about an hour and I felt elated. What a terrific sense of achievement to have participated fully and consciously, how fulfilling and joyous it had been and how proud I felt that her distress had been so little and her arrival so gentle.

The secret of this personal birth success was a combination of good antenatal preparation and sympathetic and uninterfering management which enabled me to make all the pain productive and positive.

For those who might wonder about the temperament of this Leboyer baby – after seven months of being utterly angelic and placid she metamorphosed within two weeks into a bossy little bundle with a great sense of what she wanted and hasn't looked back since!

PART III

WHAT IS BIRTH LIKE FOR THE BABY?

'The child's flesh is tender, soft, flaccid. Children that are newborn should be swathed in roses ground with salt. The roof of the mouth should be rubbed with one's finger wet in honey, to cleanse and comfort the inner part of the mouth, and also to excite and to kindle the child's appetite. And he should be oft bathed and annointed with oil of myrtle or of roses and all the limbs should be annointed and rubbed with this oil.'

(Bartholomaeus' advice to mediaeval parents)

Birth is not only an experience for the parents but for the baby who is coming to life too. In concentrating exclusively on the mother's and father's psychology on the one hand, or on hospital procedures and the routine practices which often make of birth something that seems to happen on an assembly line on the other; it is easy to forget the baby's special needs. These basic needs are not only for physical care, but for an environment in which its spontaneous urges to move, to look around, to fix its eyes on the shining eyes of its mother, to root and suckle, and above all to communicate, to give and respond to human signals, are able to take place smoothly. A newborn baby is not just a passive little package, a bundle of flesh, muscles, nerves and other tissues, but a living, sentient, social being from the first moments of life. If it is treated like a hunk of meat or an inanimate doll it is being as inadequately cared for in human terms as the baby who is allowed to get too cold or who is not fed. Human beings have the right to be treated like human beings from the very beginning.

Frédérick Leboyer[1] has focused attention on the baby's

1. *Birth Without Violence*, Fontana, 1977.

experience and on the way in which we welcome or fail to welcome our babies into the world. The baby is pressed and squeezed out of the uterus and down the birth canal in a relentless way, pummelled and gripped and twisted in its progress in a manner which may be just as painful and distressing for the child as the contractions are for the mother who is giving birth. When there is pressure on the umbilical cord, oxygen-bearing blood is temporarily cut off or reduced in supply and the baby probably has a reduced awareness of what is happening. But in normal, vigorous labour the baby is a feeling participant in the act of birth, one who probably makes active head rocking and creeping movements to assist its progress down the birth canal and is not just a passive passenger.

Leboyer is concerned about what he sees as the baby's ordeal and talks about the child being 'crushed in the birth canal' as it is 'thrust into this hell', and even goes so far as to call the mother who is subjecting her baby to this trauma 'the enemy' and 'a monster'.[1] One might think that if labour is harmful to babies, Caesarean section is the answer and out of kindness we ought to refuse to have our babies vaginally. Yet a baby who is just lifted out of the mother's body through an incision in the abdominal wall tends to be less alert to respond to life and usually requires some extra stimulus to breathe.

In normal labour the uterus massages the baby with each contraction, pressing amniotic fluid out of the respiratory passages so that they are clear to take in air with the first breath at delivery, and vigorously stimulating every part of the baby's body so that it slips out of the birth canal ready to respond to the challenge of living and alert to adapt to its new environment.

Leboyer is highly critical of routine practices and thoughtless and insensitive behaviour in the delivery room which result in rough handling of the baby, loud noises and uncoordinated, hurried movements. In many hospitals the haste

1. Op. cit.

to complete the third stage of labour, clear up, suture the perineum after the episiotomy and get the mother to the ward still take precedence over more human considerations, and the bonding of not only mother and baby but of father and baby is allowed to take place only within a restricted space of time when they are permitted to hold their baby.[1] This is terminated by whisking the baby away to the nursery to be examined by the paediatrician, and the mother may not see her child again for several hours or even longer. The unspoken message is clear: 'If you are going to be a good mother and are not going to mistreat your baby we must give you time for holding the baby, but this has to fit into hospital routines and only requires a few minutes or so.' Moreover, concern about possible baby battering means that now staff watch new mothers to see if they are bonding 'correctly' during this time, as if an examination in motherhood is being conducted in the minutes following delivery. I believe that while there is a real advantage in staff being sensitive to the nuances of the interaction between the mother and her new baby, this can only be achieved when there is understanding and compassion and should never become a mere bald notation of facts like 'Mother refused to hold baby' or 'Mother said, "What an ugly little thing!" ' There is a great deal more to the first meeting of mother and baby than that!

Leboyer believes that the baby should be greeted in silence, born into stillness and peace where no noise intrudes on the infant's first sensory contact with the world outside the uterus. He also suggests that lights should be dimmed so that no harsh light blinds the baby as it first attempts to open its eyes. Newborn babies are not blind, but blinded. Lighting in hospital delivery rooms is often excessively bright not only for the baby but also for the mother who is sometimes expected to labour with lamps shining full in her face. Though attendants at the delivery may want a bright spotlight on the perineum so that they can see exactly what is happening at delivery and can observe the baby closely, this can be turned

1. Sheila Kitzinger, *The Good Birth Guide* (Fontana, 1979).

231

off immediately following the birth and there is rarely any need to have bright lighting throughout the room. In my experience babies differ in the way they respond to light at delivery, and some babies immediately screw up their eyes as if in pain and open them only when lights are dimmed. Since the baby needs to open its eyes to get in touch with its world, harsh lighting hampers it in its first reaching out to begin to know the environment.

The silence is another matter. The woman who wants a Leboyer-style delivery may feel inhibited about crying out in joy as her baby is delivered and both father and mother may be told, 'sh, sh, sh' as they shout with wonder and delight as their baby bursts into life. I believe that to suppress spontaneous emotional expression during this peak psychological experience can do nothing but harm and that its denial must affect interaction between mother, father and baby in a negative way.

Because childbirth is for the woman a psychosexual experience, the emotional peak attained when her baby slips into life, the sense of physical release and the extraordinary feeling of the warm, wet, firm body between her legs is often accompanied by involuntary sounds of astonishment and pleasure and sometimes ecstasy. To interrupt or forbid these is to interfere in a climactic experience which is no less vivid and intense because it is the birth of a baby rather than the peak of sexual intercourse.

The act is completed in fulfilment and in a satisfaction which is the deeper because it is not only intellectual knowledge that the baby is here, nor only emotional in the sense that there is joy at welcoming the new life, but also intensely *physical*. The physical reality of childbirth, experienced in her body in the full drama of creation, is an integral part of the emotions that lead the mother to reach down to draw her baby into her arms and to know that she belongs to the child and the child to her.

Moreover, sound is not new to the baby. While inside the uterus the baby has been able to hear many sounds inside its

232

mother's body and others coming from the outside world. These are conducted readily through the amniotic fluid in which the baby is lying, but because it also fills the middle ear they are probably muffled. Anyone who has heard Dr Murooka's [1] sounds of the mother's blood vessels chugging away will be aware that the baby is accustomed to a steady beat from the maternal aorta and clearly it must also hear the rumblings and bursts of rhythmic activity in her digestive tract. The baby responds to loud noises coming from outside too. When a study was done in Warsaw over the Polish national holiday doctors found that the babies' heart rates changed every time cannon fired. They thought at first that this might have happened because the mothers were startled by the noise, so they fixed up the mothers with earphones so that they could listen to music and then used a tuning fork over their abdomens to discover whether the babies reacted to sounds.

Research showed that the fetus does respond to noise of specific kinds of intensity, pitch and tone, as any mother realises who has noticed how her baby moves when she is listening to music, especially when cymbals clash or when sound reverberates. Dr Michel Odent, working in Pithiviers, France, actually has singing groups for couples during pregnancy because the audiologist in his team finds that certain kinds of musical sound are most likely to stimulate a response in the fetus. [2] She calls these sounds 'pelvic' because they appear to resonate in the cavity of the pelvis. It is almost as if the baby dances in reaction to them. Dr Michèle Clements in London has discovered that the fetus actually appears to show preference for some kinds of music and that the same music when played to the newborn is most likely to soothe a crying baby. [3]

1. *Sleep Gently In the Womb*, E.M.I.
2. *Bien Naître* (Seuil, 1976).
3. 'Observations on certain aspects of neonatal behaviour in response to auditory stimuli', paper delivered at 5th Int. Congress of Psychosomatic Obst. & Gynec., Nov. 1977, Rome.

It seems that the uterus, far from being silent and completely cut off from the world, a pitch dark cave isolated in the recesses of the mother's body, is actually a busy, bustling place where light filters through shadows and occasionally irradiates the outer dome, and which hums with noise both from the mother's own internal organs and from her voice and the voices and other sounds connected with activity going on around her. All this suggests that receiving the newborn baby into complete silence could be more of a shock than greeting it with human speech.

The baby is already familiar with the cadences of its mother's voice and probably also with those of its father. Viewed in this light, nothing could be better than to welcome the child with its parents' own excited voices, and then for the mother to draw the baby up into her arms and nestle it close to her heart where it can hear the regular beat of a sound which it already knows well.

Dr Odent calls other intrusive, distracting sounds which are a normal part of life in a hospital 'parasitic' and believes that these are the ones which it is important to eradicate: heavy footsteps, instruments dropped in a kidney dish, voices of command, doors banging, telephones ringing, the impersonal sound of the intercom, squeaking, clattering trolleys and the chatter of people who are not focused on the reality of this unique moment as a baby comes to life and gazes at its parents for the first time.

The baby can hear most readily sound which corresponds to the tone of the human voice and especially the pitch of a woman's voice. When she speaks directly to her baby the mother often quite unconsciously raises the pitch of her voice so that it is several notes higher than her usual speaking voice. Not only the mother does this, but other women do it too; they are speaking in normal voices and then one turns to the baby and says, 'Hello, sweetie you're a nice baby, a poppet!' and suddenly her voice is dramatically different, pitched precisely to elicit the best response from the newborn baby. Men do this too, but perhaps more rarely. In a tape recording of one of my own children's births my husband can be heard first speaking to me, 'Oh darling, how wonderful!' and then he addresses his little daughter, 'What shall we call you, little thing?' in a completely different and much higher voice. All this happens quite spontaneously and people who are interacting with a baby do not have to be taught how to do it. The important thing is that they should be in an environment which, because of its human warmth and friendliness, facilitates this kind of interaction. I believe that it is this, not silence or hushed voices, which provides the most appropriate setting for birth and the introduction of the newborn infant to life.

Leboyer also advises massaging the baby, something he does himself in his film *A Child is Born* [1] for a prolonged period of time while the mother lies and waits for her baby to be handed to her. Many women consider this an unnecessary and undesirable intrusion on the meeting of mother and child and would much prefer to be given their babies immediately. If the naked baby goes straight to the mother's arms she will touch her child in just the right way; she explores it, strokes the head and limbs, feels the plump firmness of its body, shapes and cradles the curves of cheeks, shoulders, buttocks. She starts with feathery, slight, tentative movements, touches the little clenched fist, traces the line of the brow, the curve of an ear, but soon proceeds to much bolder squeezing and embracing.

She is getting to know her baby through touch. This is not just something done to the baby for a therapeutic purpose but the beginning of the communication which will develop and continue for the rest of their lives together. It is part of a continuum and as such I believe that it is more important than any ritual performed on the baby by other people, however caring and however skilled.

Leboyer also teaches that the cord should not be clamped until it has stopped pulsating. Midwives have usually in the

1. Available through the Birth Centre, 16 Simpson St., London, S.W.1. Tel: 01 223 7076.

past waited for all available blood to be conveyed to the baby from the placenta before clamping it. It is only with the new high speed deliveries which are becoming accepted as the norm in modern hospitals that doctors and midwives tend to clamp and cut immediately the baby is delivered.

R. D. Laing [1] believes that early clamping of the cord, before the baby has started breathing on its own, must cause trauma and asserts that in psychoanalysis he has encountered many suffering people who, when early childhood and infant memories are relived, recount a sudden shock and pain following birth which he connects with the cutting off of the blood supply to the newborn baby. All such experiences are remembered and stored in the organism, he believes, and the long term results can be anxieties which affect cardiac rhythms and breathing functions. Such events may underlie otherwise inexplicable allergies, upper respiratory tract infections, asthma and phobias of being in an enclosed space.

It would be very difficult to prove or to disprove psychological insights of this kind, but there is a strong case for so arranging birth and the introduction to life that the baby is not heedlessly exposed to unnecessary pain and shock. There is no reason why the first moment of living should be made an ordeal for the baby.

Leboyer also recommends that the baby be put in a warm bath where it returns to the watery medium which it has just left and can begin to discover its own body and look around. The bath is the part of the welcome which hospital staff in Britain most criticise, suggesting that there is a real risk of hypothermia in the newborn unless it is warmly wrapped or put under a heater. Certainly newborn babies, especially tiny ones, can lose heat rapidly, and it is important that not only is the water comfortably warm to the elbow, but that the surrounding air in the room is warm and without draughts since the baby's greatest area of heat loss is the

1. Speaking to the British section of the International Society for Psychosomatic Medicine in Obstetrics and Gynaecology, October 1972.

head, which is large compared with the rest of its body. Even in a modern hospital where the temperature in the delivery room is kept at an oppressively high degree, ventilation ducts may blow cold air over the baby. If the bath is to be given it must be placed well away from gusts of cold air and since extra hot water cannot safely be introduced once the baby is in the bath, yet the temperature must be carefully controlled, it may be best for the bath to be lined with insulated material to retain the warmth. In fact, it is possible to use a box such as is sold for carrying picnic food and keeping it either hot or cold. This done, objections to the bath on the grounds that the baby might become dangerously chilled can be over-ridden.

In the Leboyer film it is Leboyer himself who baths the baby. There seems to be no reason why a doctor should be any more skilled at bathing a baby than the father or mother, and where the bath is done it is usually the father of the baby who takes over, with the help of a midwife who gives him confidence and emotional support. Fathers to whom I have talked who have done this have very much enjoyed it and have relished this first contact with their babies. Sometimes the mother has felt a bit out of it and longed to receive the baby back into her arms. In Julian Aston's film *Birth*,[1] the mother waits expectantly, almost 'hovers' as she watches her husband bath their baby, and to the observer there seems a great space between the baby in the bath at the end of the bed and the mother craning her neck to see what is going on. One suggestion is for the bath to be done right beside the mother's bed where she too can touch the baby and cradle it in the water.

From the father's point of view, giving the bath provides an opportunity for relating to the baby, which some men find difficult at first. Dr Odent told me that he did not think the bath so necessary for the baby but that something important happened in the man. I watched one man, who had wanted

1. Available from the National Childbirth Trust, 9 Queensborough Terrace, London, W2 3TB. (Tel: 01-229-9319/9310).

to dash off after the delivery to tell his mates, cradle his baby in the warm bath and as he did so the baby opened its eyes and looked straight at him; he looked down at his child and it seemed that in that moment a *father* was born.

But there are other questions about the Leboyer bath which express many women's sense of unease about the introduction of any ritual which interferes in their initial relationship with the newborn baby and deprives them of the chance to hold the child for as long as and in any way they wish. Women wonder whether the baby may not be equally comfortable and 'unfold' in the same way if it is simply left lying on the mother's body and whether skin contact may not be even more valuable than trying to recreate the conditions in the uterus which the baby has just left. Certainly the movements made by a baby resting on its mother's abdomen or breast are very similar to those of a baby in bath water, provided that the environment is peaceful and everyone allows time to stand still while the baby makes its first important discoveries about the world.

We need to review the culture of childbirth which we have come to accept in our society as normal and to create a new kind of birthing. Frédérick Leboyer has contributed something of inestimable value in directing our attention to the way in which we welcome our babies into the world and in reminding us of the importance of consideration and gentleness. He has raised important questions about how we greet the newborn and about the manner in which it is handled. But the answers we give to the questions he asks of us may well be different from those he provides himself, and the silent delivery and the ritual bath conducted by the doctor may not seem to us to provide the right environment for birth for either the baby or the mother.

In becoming alert to the baby's needs it is also easy to forget the woman who is bearing the child, and the new concern with how the baby is treated at birth can be yet another way in which men tell women what they should do; another way in which 'experts' further sap our self-confidence.

It seems that Leboyer has little faith in the mother's ability to introduce the world to her child, resting it against her body and massaging it quite spontaneously with hands which reach out to hold it close and explore every tiny part. In fact, women do know what to do if they are *themselves* given love and support and a chance to hold their babies immediately. Provide the right environment for the mother, and the baby is greeted and touched and explored in just the right way.

But if the mother's emotional needs are neglected, if she feels she is merely the container from which the baby is removed, in spite of and not because of herself, she is unable to 'give' to her baby. If she finds herself in a loveless atmosphere, everything that is done to the baby, massage, bathing, music or whatever, is no more than ritual magic which fails to nourish the relationship between the mother and child that is just coming into being, which is what really matters in the all-important first hour after delivery.

It is women who bear the babies. Perhaps it is time for women to say exactly what they would like in labour and at birth. No cult should get in the way of a mother's first-hand experience of the baby she has just pushed out into the world.

This can apply as much to the cult of the ritual bath as to the technological cult of birth in what all too often looks like a well-equipped torture theatre. There is nothing to compare with giving birth without haste or cheer-leading among friends in an atmosphere of peace where the mother is encouraged, quite simply, to do whatever she *feels* like doing.

THE PARENTS' FEELINGS ABOUT THE BABY

The new-born baby is a wonderfully constructed but often raw looking little creature, and not all mothers welcome their offspring with the delight which they think they ought to feel.

This slippery wine-red object slides out of the body screeching, wet, sticky, with a drop or two of blood on the forehead or in the matted hair, perhaps a white creamy substance – vernix – clinging to the skin, and bruises on the eyelids or between the eyes. The head has been moulded, like a ripe grapefruit, by its journey out of the uterus and down the birth canal, and the forehead slopes far back, like drawings of Neanderthal man. There may be a large blister or bump slightly to one side of the crown of the head where the baby was pressed down against an as yet incompletely dilated cervix.

The mouth may be a rosebud – or soft and wet like an old man's, and the hair abundant and frequently growing in extraordinary places as if nature had started off to make a monkey and then changed its mind, or sparse as if only the rudiments of humanity were being provided and the parents must make do with that.

The genitals seem extraordinarily large for such a small baby, and look distended beneath the umbilical cord, jelly-like, white and blue and rather uncanny.

Before the child takes its first great gasp of air the body and faces are often purplish-blue, the chest wall caved in and the muscles slack. Then, with the inhaled air and the first animal-like cry or bleat, the lungs inflate and the baby may turn a brilliant red.

He clutches at the air with star-fish fingers and long

arched feet, flexing and extending his limbs as air, cold, light and noise hit him, as the body at last slithers completely free from the confines of the uterus.

The kicking bundle the mother felt inside her is suddenly confronting her and demanding life – a being often unlike anything she imagined. It is not her, or a part of her, any longer, but aggressively *other*.

To the husband it may seem incomprehensible that this baby – obviously a stranger to him – is also a stranger to her. After all, it has lived nine months in her body. She has felt every kick and stretching movement. She has said – oh so many times – 'His feet are just there, under my right ribs.' She has known when he slept and when he woke. And yet, after all this, she still confronts him with astonishment, and even with alarm.

Helene Deutsch points out that: ... 'In the last weeks of pregnancy ... the relationship with the child is split: the being in the uterus already has his double, who is the subject of all expectations and fantasied wish fulfilments and whose real existence as a distinct person is gradually approaching ... With the cutting of the physical umbilical cord ... the mother receives a real substitute for what until then has been only a fantasy, an illusion.' [1]

In pregnancy the 'real' baby is the baby inside, and the baby that is to be is a shadow child. In the final weeks things change, and the baby about to be born becomes a larger, and even sometimes a menacing, shadow; what will it be like? Will it be normal? 'I have let myself feel soft and loving about it, allowed myself to be all wrapped up in dreams of the baby and in the comforting closeness of it during these waiting months, but ... suppose it really is awful and I can't love it? Suppose I want nothing to do with it?' In the middle of the night the pregnant woman can wake and lie with half-formed thoughts like these floating in and out of her mind. There are thus two babies in her world – not one – right at the end of

1. *Psychology of Women: Psychoanalytic Interpretation.* 2 vols. (Heinemann, 1944).

pregnancy: the baby that is kicking and squirming inside – felt as real, but still not really known – and the other fantasy child – the baby that is to be. And in the last weeks, and during labour, the mother is moving away from the first and inexorably towards her meeting with the second. Her willingness or unwillingness to do this may permeate her whole attitude to her labour. Once the baby is there, part of the problem of adapting to motherhood is to reconcile the fantasy with reality, and somehow to fuse these two babies into one. The initial task of good care after the birth must obviously be to see that both mother and baby are safe. But after that the task is simply this: to see that the optimum conditions are created for a mother to learn about her baby, and to let her idea of the baby-inside-her grow into and merge with the reality of the baby-in-her-arms. All else – feeding the child enough and bathing and changing it, and knowing how to handle it – will then follow quite naturally, with trial and error perhaps; but gradually a pattern of caring for the baby will evolve, and the days which at first seem so formless and so full of feeds will begin to have order in them again.

Meanwhile the new mother looks at the baby's bright eyes, like a bird's, shining clear but not knowing her. The skin is creased like the crushed petals of a rose, but with fine down on it; she looks at the carefully delineated eyebrows, the shell-like fingernails, each separate stippled eyelash. The baby grips her finger, grasping on to life itself. It is born with this reflex to hang on, just as the monkey baby grips the mother's fur or the branch of a tree. It is the grasp which gave the Spartan baby a chance of life as it hung suspended over a precipice. It will gradually fade, but just at the moment the newborn child clings to the mother.

And not only with his hand. If the breast is near and the baby's cheek against it, he may begin to root around for the nipple. Finding it, the tongue curls under the nipple, and he presses his jaws firmly around both nipple and the brownish circle framing it, and starts to suck, as if with inbuilt knowledge that his survival depends on his ability to do this. The sucking reflex of a healthy newborn baby who is put straight to the breast is often astonishingly strong. It is as if the child had been waiting for just this opportunity – had struggled to birth simply for this, and at last found his home. Even if he is not offered the breast, he may find his fingers or thumb and suck as he was probably sucking *in utero*, alone and uncomforted.

For the mother, too, it is important that she has the chance not only of seeing and hearing, but also of handling the baby. It is not enough for him to be put down snug in a cot beside her. She needs to be able to touch and explore his body, and see that her child is perfect. If she is not given this opportunity she may lie feeling estranged from the child, uncertain even, especially if she drifts between sleep and waking after a difficult delivery, whether she has in fact given birth, or whether the child is still in her body, unconvinced of the baby's health and completeness, and rapidly losing confidence in her ability to be a mother. This can happen particularly with premature babies or any newborn needing special care, when the experts take over and the mother is left with her arms empty. When at last she is required to care for her baby she may become anxious and fearful, guilty at her own incapacity, and over-protective, a pattern of mothering which may persist in her relationship with the child she bore, right through until that child is adult.

Every mother needs time when she is alone with her baby and unselfconscious – not under the watchful eye of nurse or doctor, or mother and mother-in-law, but when she can quietly begin to get to know her baby, living in the here and now of close physical contact, safe from the proddings of what she ought to do, of how the baby 'ought' to behave. She need not do things to him, or perform any active caring function: it is enough simply that they are together. The father too deserves this breathing-space. He does not have to prove that he can bath the baby, or change his nappy with all the professional skill of the Sister who took the antenatal class; he should be able to hold the baby in his own way and enjoy his own kind of dexterity. If a man knows how to handle a woman tenderly he should be able to handle a baby. A woman has only to think of the pleasure her husband can give her, to realise that he has his own kind of sensitivity and gentleness.

In hospitals today the father may be the man standing by the bed but he is rarely the man in it. Perhaps if we had special family rooms with large beds in which mother, father and baby could lie together in privacy, both parents could relate to the baby in their own way and at their own speed without the intervention of any rituals designed to 'ensure' bonding. After the first few hours of life babies need something more than handling gently, a peaceful environment and loving care; they benefit, like monkey babies, from stimulation – from being talked and sung to, rocked, rubbed and patted, and later still, being bounced and swung – and this the father is usually expert at doing.

To the new mother, who has, like the child, passed over the bridge of birth, and whose body is now empty of the new-found life, there may be no jubilation or explosion of happiness. And even though relatives and spectators may prod her to express the appropriate emotions, she may simply feel weary, achingly empty and lost, and unable to feel that the baby really belongs to her, or even that she wants it to.

This occurs particularly when the baby is taken from her to a nursery, and is not left close where she can explore it – not only with her eyes but with her fingers, checking that every part is there, stroking the soft down on his head, feeling the strength and vitality of the limbs, the mushroom-cushioned firmness of the little buttocks, the delicate whorls of the convoluted ears – which are somehow very obvious in a newborn baby and look as if they have something to reveal about its personality. 'It's Uncle Arthur's ears', they say, or 'Lucy's feet', as if every part must be traced to some other person's ownership, be accounted for – and the baby must be thus incorporated into the family, fixed to the tree of familial inheritance securely and for ever. The mother may start to look for these resemblances too, and then suddenly feel tired of the game and intensely irritated by it. This is *her baby*, and nothing like Emily or John or Granny.

But just now she may be looking at it with something approaching horror, both at its own appearance and strangeness, and her own reactions. For it looks like none of the pictures in the baby books she so assiduously studied, cuddly, smooth and scented with the special powder, shawl-swathed, firmly encased in the conventional wrapping of human dress. It is something outlandish and weird, its face bearing all the signs of senility rather than newness, scarlet as a boiled lobster, its shriek animal-like; it stops crying and she listens to the jerky, spasmodic breathing, the little sighs, grunts and starts, and not surprisingly, she does not feel that she is a 'born mother'. Her own reactions may alarm and depress her, making her feel afraid of her inner thoughts. She ought, she feels, to be overwhelmed with thanksgiving and love – and there is only this!

This is when she needs reassurance: that very new mothers frequently feel like this, and that there is nothing abnormal about the child. The love affair with the baby may be sudden and cataclysmic the moment it is laid in her arms, may slowly dawn over the days following delivery – or hit her a week or so after the birth with all the immediacy and urgency of a first falling in love.

A mother needs a chance to get to know her baby just as one has to get to know anybody else in an intimate (and demanding) personal relationship. This knowledge does not come overnight. The mother does not *instinctively* know how to hold or carry him, and when she acts spontaneously with the comfortable assurance that she is doing the right thing, this is because she has learned how to do so. Much of this learning is informal, and unselfconscious, and is a result of noticing how other women handle their babies, or even how her own mother or an aunt handled a baby when she was a small girl herself, and of childhood play with dolls, or caring

245

for animals or younger siblings. In different societies this handling is different, and the mother's spontaneous way of holding the child, settling it on her back or hip, in the fold of a shawl, or in a carry-cot or pram, and the way she washes it and feeds it, will reflect these actions of other women – which she has absorbed, and which have become part of her maternal behaviour. In primitive and peasant societies maternal behaviour tends to be relatively unreflective and unintellectualised. The mother rarely questions her actions or pauses to think why, when or how she should perform a certain action. If the sociologist or other research worker stops her and questions this behaviour, I have seen how, in the West Indies, she either finds the query hilariously irrelevant or begins to lose self-confidence.

In modern Western society women feel they can learn from the experts and often start off with far less confidence than does the peasant mother. They only have to be told, 'Do it like this dear' or 'Do you think he is getting enough milk from you?' to be assailed in a highly vulnerable spot.

An anthropologist knows that there is no 'right' way of bathing a baby – only a great many fascinatingly different ways. In my classes I emphasise these cross-cultural aspects of child care and mothering, because it helps the new mother if she can dare to be a little experimental in her approach to baby care, and her basic task is to learn from the child, rather than to superimpose upon him techniques which she has acquired from a book or from watching a demonstration. Parenthood – no less than infancy and childhood – is a learning process. The baby has not read the books, however good they are, and the only thing the mother can do is to learn from the child himself. Any other course is fraught with frustration and failure.

I realised when I read through these labour reports that the mothers writing in these pages do not report on feelings of horror when they first see their babies. Most insist that they are absolutely beautiful. This is a pity in a way, because it makes them all seem 'natural mothers', whereas I am sure

246

they were not. Perhaps the fact that we talked a good deal about maternal (and paternal) feelings, the appearance of the new baby, and the mother–child relationship in its less positive as well as its immediately rewarding aspects, meant that these women were not readily shocked by the baby, or their own reactions to it.

But they do make it clear that they felt the need to touch and explore their babies and to feed them when they cried. Various mothers reported verbally that they ran into difficulties when they tried to conform to a rigid feeding schedule demanded by the hospital. Many hospitals are relaxed about schedules nowadays, but understaffing, or lack of flexibility in methods of post-natal care of mother and baby, can mean that mothers find themselves in a situation of conflict, and if this is likely a 48-hour-discharge arranged beforehand seems the sensible thing when possible.

When a baby is removed to the nursery to be watched for a couple of days after a forceps delivery or a Caesarean section (which is routine in many hospitals, and does not mean that the baby is ill) a mother sometimes faces special problems of relating to her baby, and may harbour anxious fears about it and her capacity as a mother.

The more a woman feels unable to cope, the more urgent is her need to get to know the infant, and the more she should be encouraged to have the baby in the vicinity, so that when she feels ready she can do things for it. If someone else takes over she is only confirmed in her feelings that she is inadequate as a mother. This is equally true of women suffering from mental breakdown after childbirth, as experience at the Cassell Hospital has shown. Babies are amazingly tough, and stand up to unskilled handling and flourish on it. Only thus can the mother gradually grow in confidence, understanding – and tenderness.

Some of the mothers having second babies whose stories are told here had been through this with the first, and talked about their feelings in class. These women often needed extra support after the baby was born, and when this was given were able to breastfeed their second babies successfully.

Once the baby is delivered, its existence outside the warmth and comfort of its mother's body is in some ways a continuation of life in the uterus. Although the break appears sudden and dramatic, caring for the baby and answering its needs requires conditions which echo that of intrauterine life. The baby is one of the most helpless of newly delivered creatures, unable like a baby kangaroo to burrow inside its mother's pouch, or to struggle to its feet and follow its mother like a foal. In its nakedness it seems about as vulnerable as a new-hatched baby bird.

In the uterus the baby was comfortably warm, rocked in the cradle of the pelvis as the mother moved, near her heart, and presumably, since the fetus is known to respond to sound, able to hear her heart-beats (and also the sound-effects of the digestive machinery!), fed without effort on its part, kept clean in the amniotic fluid, able to move and exercise within a limited area, and in darkness, and protected from infection by the placenta. In fact, it was the placenta, the baby's 'tree of life', which performed many of these functions involving nutrition and the getting rid of waste material, and when the baby is born the mother takes over the work of the placenta and the other organs which automatically cared for her baby.

Many of the problems that crop up in the early weeks reflect a mother's – or someone else's – inability to respond sensitively to the baby's needs, and as far as possible to re-create initially the conditions of life in the uterus. Sometimes she is determined, on the contrary, to make the infant 'fit in' – to socialise and train it before it is ready to learn. The result is usually a great waste of energy, and in the first few months the baby is either 'broken', or starts fighting the mother, and they both get embroiled in a conflict about feeding, or sleeping, or pot-training, or all these three together.

All babies cry, at least sometimes – on average, it has been estimated, about two hours a day. This usually means

248

they need feeding, perhaps holding and cuddling. But some babies cry anyway. Try turning the wireless on or doing some vacuum cleaning near by. It is impossible to make a baby sleep, but it is often easier for the baby to sink into sleep if you have a background of rhythmic sound which, perhaps because it is closer to the conditions the baby experienced inside the uterus, may have a more soporific effect than complete silence. Any household machine, music or a background of human conversation can do this. It may be the origin of the lullaby, which uses the frequencies of the human voice combined with a rhythmic and musical cadence. The mother can make and adapt her own lullabies and it does not matter if they are nonsense.[1]

Babies who cry a great deal, often for hours every evening, are usually said to have 'three month colic' – really 'paroxysmal fussing'. This does not mean that the mother is inadequate or is doing anything wrong, but the baby is obviously claiming more attention, and needs it, and it is an effective way of him letting his loneliness, and his need for being cuddled, be known. Sometimes these babies are getting their food fast, but need much more sucking time. The answer may be a dummy. It is doubtful whether wind is the reason, although a crying baby will produce wind simply because he has inhaled air while crying; it is the effect rather than the cause.

There are on the market various types of papoose sling which allow the mother to carry the baby around with her whilst she gets on with her work, rather as an African mother quite naturally does. The closeness and the jogging movement often make the baby much happier. If the worst comes to the worst the frantic parents can get in the car and drive the baby round, as most babies adore motoring and immediately fall asleep, only to wake and cry whenever the car stops at traffic lights.

One of the things over which the modern woman can get

1. *The Experience of Breastfeeding*, Sheila Kitzinger (Penguin 1979).

most fraught is how, when and on what to feed the baby. It is as if nutrition epitomises motherhood, and as if her capacity to be a good mother is dependent on her ability to get sufficient milk into the baby, through the processes of digestion, and the waste products out the other end, without mishap. To a man this emphasis on the nutritional and excretory may seem overdramatised and inexplicable. But for a woman who is unsure of herself as a mother it symbolises the weight of responsibility that she has taken on for this new life, this utterly dependent baby.

The middle class mother in our society today is the one most likely to want to breast-feed, but even though she may be determined to show that she can do it, this determination cannot by itself produce milk, and is in fact not a good basis for the relaxed and casual feeding which is the dominant pattern all over the world where breast-feeding is most successful. Whereas she no longer believes that intercourse involves merely her tacit acceptance of male advances, and then lies still and thinks of England, attitudes to breast-feeding are still infused with notions about clocks and timing, about getting the wind up, and even with pseudo-hygienic practices involving washing nipples with soap and water before and after feeds. Any woman who really wants to can breast-feed (with the very rare exception) and she probably would if she were alone on a desert island and left to experiment and work it out for herself[1]

Whereas it is usually safe to bottle feed, the safest method of all is to breast-feed – not only because the baby is far less likely to get gastro-enteritis, and because there is still the occasional allergy to cow's milk, but for other reasons: a baby is more likely to be immune to various illnesses its mother has had if breastfed; he can absorb the calcium in his mother's milk much more easily than in cow's milk (very low calcium can lead to tetany); and breast milk has five times the amount of Vitamin C as *unboiled* cow's milk. Of course, most of these disadvantages can be remedied by adding

1. *The Experience of Breastfeeding*, op. cit.

things to cow's milk, and the bottlefed infant thrives. But again and again we see how, as we move farther away from the natural and spontaneous, we run into dangers and take risks which science and technology can only elaborately and painstakingly counteract by yet new inventions which, whilst solving some problems, at the same time produce new dangers and risks. And in all this it is often human relationships that suffer.

The spontaneous movement and sounds that a mother makes as she rocks or talks nonsense to her baby – apparently meaningless and without pattern – are vital factors in the development of a relationship between the mother and baby, and, because this is the primal human relationship, between the child and society. Breast-feeding can be important because it involves a special sort of touch, flesh contact, and an acceptance of the child by the mother as it returns to her body – a sort of physical loving which can be just as significant for the baby and mother as the physical expression of love in marriage. For breast-feeding is a sexual activity (one reason perhaps, why some women hate it), and part of the very wide spectrum of sexuality in a woman's life, ranging all the way from her image of herself as a woman, through making love and the process of childbearing, to the different ways in which she deals with her sons and daughters as they grow up through childhood and adolescence, and her reactions to menstruation and to the menopause.

Most women who want to breast-feed welcome support from their husbands, who may have to shield them from the advice that comes in from other people (and sometimes from mothers and mother-in-law) about what they ought and ought not to do. The let-down reflex, which occurs when milk is released from the glands into the ducts, ready to pour out through tiny holes in the nipple (rather like the holes in the rose of a watering can), is closely associated with the emotions. A woman hearing a baby cry, whether or not it is her own, may feel the breasts start to tingle, and is immediately ready to give milk. On the other hand if she is feeding

251

peacefully, and someone she dislikes, or with whom she has a strained relationship, comes into the room, the milk supply may be suddenly inhibited.

The nearest analogy to favourable conditions for the new mother to learn how to breast-feed is that provided by what are commonly considered favourable conditions for love making: a comfortable warm bed, privacy, a relaxed atmosphere, and a sense of timeless leisure. And just as with intercourse, the first attempts may not bring the delight or satisfaction which was hoped for, so gradually the nursing couple, like the couple making love, learn to understand and respond to each other's needs; for breast-feeding, and indeed the whole of parenthood, is – like any form of loving – a process of discovery.

Difficulties in establishing or maintaining breast-feeding can mean that a woman feels a failure almost from the start, and that she gets involved in a struggle with the baby which may persist long after infancy.

On the other hand, the decision to breast-feed cannot, in itself, guarantee the child's or the mother's, placidity. Often in the early post-natal days latent anxieties come to the surface, and a perfectly 'normal' and apparently contented woman can wonder, as she holds the baby in the bath, what would happen if she tilted her arm just a little and let the baby's head sink under the water (and be a little tempted to do it); or when the child cries and she seems to be able to do nothing to comfort it, can have the impulse to escape – to rush out of the house and leave her tormentor. She can find herself weeping unaccountably, or tense and alert as if always listening for the least sound from the baby.

A feeling of let-down after childbirth is common, especially on about the third or fourth post-partum day – the sort of depression that can follow any big event in one's life, or even something like a party or the end of the exams. It often only lasts for a day, and is experienced more often in the alien atmosphere of hospital than after a home confinement. It is no good saying 'snap out of it', and it is much better for a woman to simply ride out the lethargy that accompanies despondency, or the tears that can be the outward sign of a storm of despair. A husband can offer a good deal of quiet emotional support by asserting his confidence in her as a mother, his love for her as a woman, and by providing a strong shoulder to weep on.

Sometimes, however, the mother and baby relationship seems to break down completely – a woman rejects her child (maybe weeks after the birth) and this is usually a sign of more serious post-natal depression, for which expert help should be sought. The new mother may feel the baby is not really hers, or hate him and try to harm him, be completely unable to face the responsibility of motherhood, and at the same time feel guilty about this. This sort of depression does not come like a bolt out of the blue. It happens to women who have known periods of severe depression before, or who frequently experience violent mood swings, and who have very often had a very unstable and unhappy childhood. Sometimes there has been no mother, and sometimes a very possessive, domineering one who has taken over her daughter's life, and lived through her, so that the girl feels she has no identity of her own, and no right to be a mother herself. Either way, she can be a very frightened woman when confronted with the demands of motherhood. She expresses this by disclaiming the responsibility through paranoid feelings that other people are out to take the baby away from her or to destroy it, or by an utter disregard of the child, as if it did not exist, or overt aggression towards it. If a couple face this sort of problem it is essential that they seek help, and are not ashamed to do so. Even severe mental illness of this type can be treated, and there are many women who went through a period, sometimes of many months, of complete irrationality and confusion who are now living useful, positive lives.

But although the new mother is the one who gets most attention, all is not necessarily plain sailing for the new father, and it is important for her to realise that he, too, may have some major emotional adjustments to make – not only in accepting added responsibility, with the financial burdens that this implies for men in our society, but also in sharing love. In some primitive societies (as for example one Amazonian Indian tribe in South America) the husband climbs into the hammock and enacts the birth instead of the wife, whilst she quietly slips away into the bush and has her baby without assistance. In some societies the 'lying in' is the husband's prerogative, and the wife gets back to cooking the porridge, doing the washing, and caring for her man and other children, whilst he lies in bed. Rituals of this type, collectively known as 'the couvade', imply that childbirth involves such change that the accompanying emotional and social transition can be helped by a visual enacting of the drama – a formalised pattern of behaviour which is marked off and completely different from the normal, everyday one and which represents values important to the society (which is really what any symbolic action does). Such rituals have significance because they have a function *vis-à-vis* the individual's relationship to others in the society. They may well have rather different meanings in each one. But their very existence points to a situation of stress. Even in Britain some psychoanalysts have examined the 'couvade syndrome' in expectant fathers – toothache, tummy-ache, loss of appetite, backache and morning sickness, and even mental illness for example – and reported that about 11% of all expectant fathers have some symptoms of psychogenic origin in relation to their wives' pregnancies.

But what of afterwards too? The arrival of a new baby in a household brings extra, and obvious, stresses; the broken nights, nappies draped over the bath when he wants to get in it, meals not ready, visitors unwelcome, a relatively unstable, vulnerable wife – laughing one moment and crying the next perhaps – and *things* around everywhere – hairbrushes, rubber sheets, plastic ducks, cots and carrycots, bottles of antiseptic and pots of baby cream. Having a baby usually means accumulating a vast array of equipment (unless the parents are able to resist the advertisements) which is all waiting to be bumped into or tripped over. No wonder that many a man feels that the baby has taken over the house and has become the dominant member of the family.

The new mother may have little time for anything or anybody else, and to a husband who is slightly jealous anyway this can provide painfully obvious evidence that she no longer loves him. The baby becomes a rival in the home, an ever-present one who loudly proclaims his presence. Not all men start off on fatherhood the secure, confident, mature individuals that the ideal of paternity suggests. A great many have periods of doubt about their own worth, their right to be loved, their potency as males, and the value of the work they are doing – times when they are just as emotionally vulnerable as their wives. A man who has experienced maternal deprivation – real or imagined – in his childhood, or who has never really solved the fundamental problems of jealousy (perhaps because he has never had any brothers or sisters and has always been the apple of his parents' eyes, or because he was protected from ever knowing that these violent feelings existed in himself) may still have to work out emotions about the baby which other men have coped with earlier in their lives.

For in many ways the battles and problems of marriage and parenthood are a continuation of other, earlier conflicts – relationships with parents and siblings, and the struggle for identity as one moves through childhood and adolescence.

There is no abrupt turning point when one suddenly emerges as a new man or woman embarking on parenthood, as a mature person. The old self is still there, with all its failings and perplexities, and has to be lived with. Yet new parents often only trace the origins of attitudes and behaviour back in moments of resentment, as a form of attack on the other: 'Your mother always did baby you! For goodness sake act your age!'

When a couple become parents they are taking on new roles. But since there is no fundamental change in the sort of people they are, it is too much for either to expect the other suddenly to turn into his or her idea of a perfect mother or father, or for that matter, for either to expect it of him or herself. Concepts of parenthood are derived largely from their own experiences in infancy and childhood, and many behaviour patterns in marriage and parenthood reflect earlier parent-child relationships. The process of becoming a parent often produces the challenge – and the opportunity – for a man and woman to grow up!

GLOSSARY

GLOSSARY OF TERMS USED IN CHILDBIRTH

This is far from being an exhaustive list and consists solely of terms women are likely to meet during pregnancy and labour. I have included, however, phrases and words other than those appearing in the text, because it may be useful for expectant parents to understand the terms and abbreviations likely to be used in their hearing. Many of these terms concern abnormalities – because when things are going well it seems that it is not so necessary to give them verbal description!

Every woman has a right to know what is taking place in and to her body, and what she can do to help. This means that she also needs to understand some of the things that can go wrong, an essential preliminary if she is to appreciate help that she is offered. It is worse than useless to think that by keeping a woman in ignorance she will not worry, or that information about her own inside and the child she is bearing has nothing to do with her. Knowledge really can cast out fear but it must be knowledge not only of pathological conditions and nature's errors, but of what can constructively be done in the situation which presents itself.

Terms are described here not so much as they would be relevant to the obstetrician, but as they relate to the women's personal experience of ante-natal procedures of labour.

ACIDOSIS The building up of acid products in the body, with resulting chemical imbalance. Ketones can be discovered in the blood and urine during a very long and tiring labour, and the woman is often given a glucose drip as a pick-me-up.

ADDUCTOR The muscle running along the inside of the upper leg.

ALBUMIN Protein which appears in the urine. It can be a sign of pre-eclampsia (which see).

AMNIOTIC FLUID The liquid in which the baby is floating in the bag of waters inside the uterus.

AMNIOSCOPE An instrument which examines the fluid around the baby by shining a minute light through the cervix in front of the baby's head.

ANTERIOR At the front. Usually in obstetrics means towards the mother's front.

APGAR RATING A quick and simple way of estimating a baby's health and responsiveness to the challenge of living based on the observation of the baby's reflex, muscle tone and breathing. Invented by Dr Veronica Apgar.

APH Ante-partum haemorrhage. Bleeding before delivery, or before labour begins (i.e. more than at the beginning of a period). The best thing is to ring the doctor or hospital, and go to bed or go into the hospital immediately.

AREOLA The pinkish brown circle around the nipple.

ARM Artificial rupture of the membranes. The doctor nicks the bag of waters (which has no nerve endings, so it does not hurt) to start off or to speed up labour.

ATTITUDE The posture of the baby in the uterus e.g. curled up, only partly curled up, or stretched out.

ANTERIOR LIP A part of the cervix still gripping the baby's head. This corresponds to transition (which see). It is a time when great patience is needed, and when the mother welcomes emotional support and encouragement.

ANOXIC Deprived of oxygen.

BRAXTON-HICKS 'Practice' contractions of the uterus felt at any time from the seventh month of pregnancy. At first noticed as brief, isolated bouts of activity, these contractions often later become regular and can be confused with true labour.

BREECH The baby's buttocks in the cervix instead of the head. An extended or frank breech is one in which the baby's legs are stretched out, with the feet somewhere about the shoulders. A flexed breech is one in which the baby is curled up in a ball.

CAUDAL One kind of regional anaesthesia (which see).

CERVIX The neck of the uterus, which hangs down in the vagina like a clapper of a bell, and thins out and then dilates during labour.

COLOSTRUM The first liquid produced by the breast in late pregnancy and following delivery. It contains gamma-globulin, which may supply antibodies for the baby, and is very high in protein (6% as compared with 1% protein in milk). It is the baby's natural first food.

CONTRACTION The shortening and thickening of a bundle of fibres when a muscle is working. In uterine contractions the longitudinal muscles are pulled up, so opening the circular muscle fibres looped like a coiled spring around the cervix.

COT NURSING A baby is cot nursed because he needs rest, warmth and minimal handling. This is often the case after an assisted delivery for 24 hours or so. It does not mean that the baby is ill.

CRESCENT A lip of cervix still round a part of the baby's head (see Anterior Lip).

DEEP TRANSVERSE ARREST This occurs in cases of posterior presentation (which see) when the baby's head becomes wedged in the hollow of the sacrum, and is unable to flex further. Forceps, or a vacuum extractor (which see), are often used to effect delivery.

DISPROPORTION A situation in which it looks as if the baby may be too big or too oddly positioned to pass through the mother's pelvis with ease. It is difficult to be certain about this until a woman is well into labour and the uterus has had a chance to show what it can do.

DISTRESS 'Fetal distress' is suspected when there is either a speeding up or a slowing down of the heart rate, or when an analysis of a drop of blood taken from the baby's skull through the dilating cervix shows a chemical imbalance.

261

This will probably mean that the obstetrician will decide to deliver quickly.

DRIP Glucose or a hormone solution is gradually dripped through a bottle down a long tube and through a fine needle into a vein of a hand or arm. This is fixed on with sticky tape, and left until after the baby is born. Apart from the initial prick, it does not hurt.

EDD Expected date of delivery. Labour may be a couple of weeks before or after this date. First babies tend to come a little bit later than second and subsequent babies.

EFFACEMENT The thinning out of the walls of the cervix until the cervix is drawn up into the main body of the uterus. This precedes labour proper, and often overlaps with the first phases of dilatation.

EMBRYO The baby in the uterus in the first three months of pregnancy.

ENDOMETRIUM The lining of the uterus.

ENDOSCOPE An instrument which measures the acidity of the baby's blood. It can be used after the membranes have ruptured. A drop of the baby's blood is sucked out through a tiny prick in the scalp, and the results are known in five minutes.

ENGAGED The biggest part of the baby's head is deep in the mother's pelvis, like an egg in an eggcup. This often occurs in the last weeks of pregnancy, but sometimes not until labour is under way.

ENGORGEMENT Often when the milk is first secreted, on about the third day after birth, the breasts become swollen, hard and hot. This can be relieved by cold compresses and by putting the baby to the breast. It soon settles down if the baby is fed whenever he wants to be.

EPIDURAL An injection in the spine which causes loss of sensation from the waist down. The amount of movement lost varies with the anaesthetic used. Uterine action is slowed for the first 10 minutes, but in a difficult labour the uterus then relaxes better between contractions, thus improving its blood supply. The mother does not want to bear down and the bladder must be emptied by catheter. Forceps are often necessary for delivery. As the injection is topped up – through a tube left in place, the mother may not have movement of her legs for about 2 hours after delivery.

EPISIOTOMY A cut in the perineum to facilitate delivery.

EXTENSION Any part of the baby which is stretched out, for example when there is an extended arm the baby's arm is stretched out and may be slowing up labour.

FALLOPIAN TUBES The tubes branching out from either side of the uterus in which fertilisation takes place.

FH Fetal heart. On the case sheet this may be ticked after about the sixth month to indicate that it has been heard, and later in pregnancy the actual rate of the baby's heart is recorded, as it also is in labour. The normal limits of the fetal heart rate are between 160 and 120 a minute.

FLEXION Any part of the baby may be curled up. Usually the baby is completely flexed during the larger part of labour.

FETUS The baby in the uterus from the third month until delivery.

FONTANELLE The soft spot on the baby's head.

FORAMEN OVALE The opening between right and left atrium of the baby's heart, which closes after birth.

FORE WATERS The liquor (which see) in front of the baby's head.

FULL DILATATION or 'fully'. The condition of the cervix when it is open to about the size of the palm of a man's hand, including the thumb joint. This is 'five fingers', approximately ten centimetres. This terminates the first stage of labour.

FULL TERM About 40 weeks from the first day of the last period.

FUNDUS The upper part of the uterus.

GA General anaesthesia. The patient loses consciousness.

GAS AND OXYGEN This is offered by mask towards the end of the first stage when and if contractions are painful, and can be self-administered. It should be taken with contractions only.

263

GLUTEI Buttock muscles.

GRAVID Pregnant. A primagravida is a woman who is in her first pregnancy, a multigravida one who is in her second or subsequent pregnancy.

HAEMOGLOBIN H-b. The part of the blood which carries oxygen around the body. High haemoglobin means that there is enough iron present in the blood to do this. A low haemoglobin means that there is insufficient iron.

HIND WATERS The liquor (which see) behind the baby's head.

HYPEREMISIS Persistent vomiting in pregnancy.

HYPERTENSION Raised blood-pressure. This can be one sign of pre-eclampsia (which see).

HYPERVENTILATION Chemical imbalance in the blood resulting from the flushing out of carbon dioxide by over-breathing – typically, forceful heavy breathing.

INCO-ORDINATE UTERINE ACTION A disharmony in the muscles of the uterus. This produces strong contractions which fail to dilate the cervix.

INDUCTION Helping labour to start, with an ARM (which see) and syntocinon drip (see drip).

INERTIA Insufficient uterine activity. Primary inertia means weak contractions from the beginning of labour. Secondary inertia means a weakening or complete cessation of uterine contractions before the baby is delivered.

INVOLUTION The return of the uterus almost to its pre-pregnancy size and weight – from about 2 lb after delivery to about 2 oz. Breast-feeding assists this process.

JAUNDICE About a third of new-born babies go a bit yellow between the second and fifth days of life. This is even more likely if they are premature. It is called 'physiological jaundice', and there is no cause for concern. Sometimes, however, babies are jaundiced (and this usually happens within 24 hours of delivery), signalling that something is wrong, and this may be associated with rhesus incompatibility (which see). Jaundice is treated with light (photo-therapy).

LET-DOWN REFLEX A conditioned reflex stimulated by the feeling of the baby at the breast or his cries, or even simply thinking about feeding the baby. When it occurs the breasts tingle and feel warm, the nipples become erect, and the milk is secreted into the ducts.

LEVATOR ANI Muscles of the pelvic floor, round the vagina, urethra and anus, which support all the pelvic contents, and down through which the baby is born.

LIQUOR The waters in which the baby floats in the uterus. Also called the amniotic fluid.

LOCHIA Discharge after childbirth – at first red for a few days, then pink, and finally colourless.

LOW FORCEPS Delivery of the baby with forceps when the head is already on the perineum (which see).

MASKS These cover both mouth and nose, and are worn by anyone attending the mother at any stage of labour when the vulva is uncovered.

MECONIUM The first contents of the baby's bowel. A dark, greenish-black sticky substance.

MEMBRANES The bag of waters.

MID-STREAM SPECIMEN A specimen of urine acquired half-way through emptying the bladder by stopping passing water through contracting the pelvic floor muscles strongly, and then continuing into a container.

MOULDING The shaping of the baby's head by his passage down the birth canal.

MULTIPARA A woman who is bearing her second or a subsequent child. A grand-multipara is a woman who has already had four babies.

OCCIPUT The crown of the baby's head. Left occipito-anterior (LOA) is a position in which the baby is lying on the mother's left looking towards her back – the commonest presentation. Right occiputo-anterior (ROA) is one in which the baby is lying on the mother's right looking towards her back.

OEDEMA Fluid retained in the tissues causing puffiness. It may be a sign of pre-eclampsia (which see). Usually it occurs in the legs simply because the mother is hot and tired.

OESTROGEN An ovarian hormone. It maintains the growth and activity of the uterus during pregnancy, helps the mother's breasts to develop for breast-feeding, and makes connective tissues more flexible, the pelvic joints mobile, and the cervix soft. After birth it causes milk to be secreted into the ducts.

OVARIES The female egg cell 'factory' and storage house situated at the end of the fallopian tubes (which see).

OVULATION The time when the egg cell ripens – normally about half-way between two periods.

PALPATION Feeling the position of the baby through the abdominal wall.

PARIETAL The bones fitting like a cap and forming the top of the skull. In the new-born baby they are separated by a suture running from back to front, and this means that as the baby's head is pressed down through the birth canal it is moulded, and the parietal bones can move slightly towards each other.

PARACERVICAL A pain-killing injection given around the cervix.

PELVIC FLOOR The muscles around the vagina, uretha and anus which support the bladder and uterus, and down through which the baby is born.

PELVIS The bony framework within which the baby lies. The front is formed by the pubic symphisis, and the back by the sacrum.

PERINEUM The soft tissue on the outside around the vagina and anus. These stretch and fan out with the descent of the baby's head, and open up with a warm, tingling sensation when the head is 'on the perineum'.

PETHIDINE and PETHILORFAN These are drugs given by injection to a woman in labour, often at about two-thirds dilatation of the cervix, which take the edge off pain and make her drowsy. They are normally given in 50 mg doses, a 'baby' dose being 50 mg, and the standard dose 100 mg. Too large a shot of either of these can result in the trained mother suffering loss of control, but used wisely they can be a great help.

PLACENTA The after-birth. It is through the placenta that the baby is nourished and receives his oxygen from the mother's bloodstream, and through it, too, he excretes waste products. The placenta has been called 'the tree of life' for the baby. It is constructed like a sponge, with blood filling the spaces. The mother's blood does not actually mix with the baby's blood, but is separated from it by a thin membrane. The placenta looks like a large piece of raw liver.

PLACENTA PRAEVIA The placenta is situated in the lower part of the uterus. When the cervix dilates, the placenta which lies over the part which is being 'taken up' starts to peel off, and this results in bleeding, commonly from the 28th week of pregnancy. This should be taken as a warning sign, and the hospital or G.P. rung immediately. A soft-tissue x-ray may be used in diagnosis, and a Caesarean section may be the best course of action.

POSTERIOR Towards the back. A posterior presentation is a baby lying with the crown of the head at the mother's back so that he is facing her front. This is also known as 'face to pubis'. Most posterior presentations are on the mother's right hand side – right occipito-posterior (ROP), although some are on the left, a left occipito-posterior (LOP). In these cases the baby's head tends to be less well flexed than with anterior presentations (which see), and a larger diameter of the baby's head is coming through the cervix and birth canal. Frequently there is a delay as the baby's head is pressed against the mother's sacrum. A woman expecting labour with a posterior should be prepared for a long first stage with backache. A persistent occipito-posterior (POP) is one in which the baby's head does not rotate into the anterior, and in which the baby is delivered looking up towards the mother instead of down towards the bed.

POSTMATURE It is very easy to be uncertain about one's dates, and no-one knows what constitutes post-maturity. But on the whole the baby more than two weeks overdue may not be receiving an adequate blood flow through the, by this time, rather elderly placenta, and the doctor will often advise inducing labour.

PR Per rectum. A rectal examination.

PRE-ECLAMPSIA Toxaemia of pregnancy. Symptoms are: raised blood pressure, albumin in the urine, puffiness of the fingers, ankles and legs, and a sudden excessive weight gain. Treatment is rest and sedation, including – very important – peace of mind, and sometimes starting labour off a little before the baby is due.

PRECIPITATE LABOUR Very rapid labour – under five hours in a woman having her first baby. There are also precipitate first and second stages.

PRESENTATION A description of the way in which the baby is lying in terms of that part of the baby which is down in the cervix. The most common is a vertex presentation (which see).

PREPARATION 'Prepping'. Having the pubic hair partially shaved, an enema or suppository to empty the lower bowel, and a bath or a shower. At the same time the blood-pressure will be taken, the midwife brings the case history up to date, listens to the baby's heart beats and checks his position. Practices vary in different hospitals.

PREMATURE or low birth weight. An international classification consisting of any babies under 2,500 g. Many Chinese and Indian babies weigh less and are full term, and this is then a better guide to whether the baby needs extra care.

PRIMIPARA A woman having her first baby.

PROGESTERONE An ovarian hormone which is manufactured by the placenta in pregnancy.

PROLAPSE Slackness in the pelvic floor muscles, which allow the bladder or uterus to drop down, with resultant low

268

backache and stress incontinence (which see). Parts of the vaginal wall can also prolapse when there has been excessive straining in the second stage. Mild prolapse can often be helped by regular pelvic floor exercises.

PSYCHOPROPHYLAXIS This has recently come to be used as a general term for any modern and systematic method of preparation for childbirth. Strictly speaking, however, it has a more specific meaning: a method of training, which historically stems from work done in the U.S.S.R. and France, based on Pavlovian theories of conditioned reflex behaviour and including 'disassociation' techniques. The term is used in the latter sense in these pages.

PUDENDAL BLOC An injection around the vagina which anaesthetises the birth outlet. This can be done before a forceps delivery and before an episiotomy (which see).

PUERPERIUM The six weeks after childbirth when the mother's body is returning to its pre-pregnancy state. A post-natal examination takes place at the end of this time.

PV Per vaginam. A vaginal examination.

PYELITIS A kidney infection. It starts with shivering and an acute pain, often on the right side, nausea or vomiting, a headache, and a sudden rise in temperature. It may occur in mid-pregnancy or after a difficult birth. With treatment it usually soon clears up.

QUICKENING The time when the mother first feels the baby's movements. This is usually between 16 weeks (with a woman who has had a baby, and knows what the flutterings are) and 20 weeks. If you are uncertain of when the baby is due, 22 weeks from quickening will give you an approximate date.

RECTAL EXAMINATION An examination through the rectum.

REGIONAL ANAESTHESIA An anaesthetic which removes sensation from only one part of the body and which is given by injection.

RHESUS All blood is either rhesus positive (i.e. contains an agglutinating factor found in the rhesus monkey) or rhesus negative. (85% of human blood is positive.) If the baby is

269

positive and the mother negative, the mother may form an antibody to the baby's blood, a bit like an allergic reaction. So blood of all expectant mothers is tested. The detailed genetic make-up of the father is also important in determining whether or not the child is likely to trigger off a reaction in the mother's blood. It is rare for the baby to be affected in the first pregnancy (unless the mother has been previously sensitised). Many Rh negative women never become sensitised at all. Haemolytic disease (haemolytic jaundice) is most likely to affect the fourth or subsequent baby of an Rh negative mother who is married to an Rh positive man who carries *both* pairs of Rh genes (that is, he is homozygous). Nowadays the Rh negative woman is given an injection after the first delivery – depending on the baby's blood group – which ensures that she will not become sensitised in later pregnancies.

ROOTING The reflex, with which the baby is born, to hunt around for the nipple.

RUBELLA German measles.

SACRUM The large bone which forms the back of the pelvis. Sacro-iliac pain is pain in the small of the back.

SECOND STAGE OF LABOUR The time from full dilatation of the cervix (which see) until delivery. This is the expulsive stage.

SEGMENT The upper part of the uterus is that part around the baby's body. The lower segment, that part around the baby's head.

SHOW A blood-stained mucous discharge which often heralds the start of labour, but may take place several days before labour actually commences. It is the plug from the cervix, and frequently there is no more show as labour progresses.

SPINAL An injection into the spine causing complete paralysis of the lower part of the body. There is no bearing down sensation. There may be a bad headache afterwards.

SPONTANEOUS DELIVERY The mother giving birth to the baby herself, without mechanical assistance from her attendants.

STRESS INCONTINENCE Wetting your pants when you cough or laugh because the pelvic floor muscles are weak.

STRIAE Stretch marks. The skin stretches from underneath, so it is not much help to rub in oil except to keep the upper layer of skin supple.

SUTURING Sewing up.

TEST FEEDING Weighing the baby before and after a feed in the same clothes. Not a good idea unless the baby is obviously ill, since it tends to increase the mother's anxiety and disturb the baby.

THIRD STAGE OF LABOUR From the birth of the baby to the delivery of the afterbirth.

TOXAEMIA (see pre-eclampsia).

TRANSITION The very end of the first stage of labour, when a tiny part of the cervix – called the 'lip' – is around the baby's head. It is often the most difficult part of labour, but may last for only a few contractions.

TRANSVERSE LIE The baby lies across the uterus. If labour is allowed to continue this may be a shoulder presentation, and it can result in obstructed labour, so the doctor turns the baby.

TRIAL OF LABOUR The term is used when there is some evidence of possible disproportion (which see) or other signs that labour may not be straightforward, so the obstetrician decides to see what the uterus can do, whilst having everything ready for a Caesarean section if necessary.

UMBILICAL CORD The cord which connects baby and placenta is about 20 inches long, consists of two arteries and one vein, and is covered with a jelly-like substance which makes it difficult for it to get knotted, especially as it is floating in liquor (which see).

VACUUM EXTRACTOR An instrument which applies suction to the baby's head and draws it down the birth canal, like a vacuum cleaner. It is most effectively used with a conscious, fully co-operative mother who can bear down at the same time as suction is applied. Also called a 'ventouse'.

VAGINAL EXAMINATION Examination through the vagina.

VERNIX The creamy substance, like cottage cheese, which protects the baby's skin, and which comes off gradually after birth. It is formed from sebum from the sebaceous glands and epidermal cells.

VERSION Turning the baby. For example, the doctor may turn a breech (which see) into a vertex (which see) by holding the baby's head and buttocks through the mother's abdominal wall and moving the baby round in the direction of its nose. It may be tried at any time from the 32nd week of pregnancy. It is very important for the mother to relax well.

VERTEX The top of the baby's head, when still inside the mother. (see Presentation.)

WALLER'S SHIELDS Plastic domes with a hole in the middle for the nipple, worn under the bra in late pregnancy to help retracted nipples stick out. Also used after the baby is born for a while if the nipples become very sore.

Expert advice for your child's first five years

Kindergarten Is Too Late

MASARU IBUKA

IS YOUR CHILD MISSING OUT?

Can a pre-school child learn foreign languages? Can he or she be taught to play a musical instrument?

Masaru Ibuka is convinced that we waste the best years of our children's lives – the years between nought and three, when, he believes, a human being's creative and learning potential is at its maximum.

This remarkable and revolutionary book presents a plan for the transformation of our entire approach to bringing up small children. It is based on the idea that small children are totally learning-oriented – and cites cases of normal two- and three-year olds being taught music and foreign languages. Mr Masaru's ideas are already being put into practice in Japan by the Early Development Association – with remarkable results. For any caring parent of a pre-school child, KINDERGARTEN IS TOO LATE is essential – and fascinating reading.

CHILDCARE   0 7221 4872 0   95p

The Mother Person

VIRGINIA BARBARA
and
MERRILL MAGUIRE SKAGGS

A guide for every mother and mother-to-be

THE JOYS – AND PROBLEMS – OF MOTHERHOOD

Of all the millions of women who have babies, it's
astonishing how few are really prepared for the upheaval
that a new member of the family causes in their lives. This
sensible, practical book is a complete guide to the realities
of motherhood. In it, you'll find chapters on:

PREGNANCY AND BIRTH – how to cope with the new
arrival

DAILY ROUTINES – feeding and care of your baby

YOUR MARRIAGE – and how it will be affected

PARENTS AND IN-LAWS – how to avoid any well-meant
interference

OLDER CHILDREN – and how jealousy can be averted

Full of down-to-earth advice designed to avoid the many
pitfalls of motherhood, this book will help any woman with
a young baby to become a true Mother Person.

CHILDCARE   0 7221 1403 6   95p

More Commonsense About Babies and Children

Dr Hugh Jolly, *The Times* paediatrician who is known to millions from his popular TV and radio programmes, once more gives us the benefit of his refreshingly down-to-earth commonsense approach.

Compiled from articles that have appeared in *The Times* over recent years, MORE COMMONSENSE ABOUT BABIES AND CHILDREN covers every aspect of childcare through pregnancy and at the moment of birth: breast-feeding, childhood ailments, the value of play, the 'difficult' child – these are just some of the topics covered in the book.

With his customary sensitivity, Dr Jolly also deals with such distressing subjects as stillbirth, infant death and baby-battering.

This is a book for parents everywhere, and for all those with a professional or personal interest in babies and children.

CHILDCARE   0 7221 5065 2   85p

And don't miss DR JOLLY'S BOOK OF CHILDCARE also available from Sphere Books.

A selection of Bestsellers from Sphere Books

Fiction

SHARKY'S MACHINE	William Diehl	£1.75	☐
THE LAST CATTLE DRIVE	Robert Day	95p	☐
VIXEN 03	Clive Cussler	£1.25	☐
THE DEATH FREAK	Clifford Irving & Herbert Berkholz	95p	☐
WOLFSBANE	Craig Thomas	£1.25	☐
PLANTATION	Maurice Denuziere	£1.50	☐
SEASON OF PASSION	Danielle Steel	£1.25	☐

Film and TV Tie-ins

THE PROFESSIONALS 5: BLIND RUN	Ken Blake	85p	☐
THE PROFESSIONALS 6: FALL GIRL	Ken Blake	85p	☐
THE PROMISE	Danielle Steel	95p	☐
BUCK ROGERS IN THE 25TH CENTURY	Addison E. Steele	95p	☐
BUCK ROGERS 2: THAT MAN ON BETA	Addison E. Steele	95p	☐

Non-Fiction

THE THIRD WORLD WAR	General Sir John Hackett	£1.75	☐
EVEREST: IMPOSSIBLE VICTORY	Peter Habeler	£1.50	☐
THE HURRICATS	Ralph Barker	£1.25	☐
LEGACY OF THE GODS	Robert Charroux	£1.50	☐

All Sphere books are available at your local bookshop or newsagent, or can be ordered direct from the publisher. Just tick the titles you want and fill in the form below.

Name...

Address...

....

Write to Sphere Books, Cash Sales Department, P.O. Box 11, Falmouth, Cornwall TR10 9EN.

Please enclose cheque or postal order to the value of the cover price plus:

UK: 25p for the first book plus 10p per copy for each additional book ordered to a maximum charge of £1.05.

OVERSEAS: 40p for the first book and 12p for each additional book.

BFPO & EIRE: 25p for the first book plus 10p per copy for the next 8 books, thereafter 5p per book.

Sphere Books reserve the right to show new retail prices on covers, which may differ from those previously advertised in the text or elsewhere, and to increase postal rates in accordance with the GPO.

(10:79)